ELECTRONIC STRUCTURE, PROPERTIES, AND THE PERIODIC LAW

Selected Topics in Modern Chemistry

SERIES EDITORS

Professor Harry H. Sisler
University of Florida
Gainesville, Florida

Professor Calvin A. VanderWerf
Hope College
Holland, Michigan

ELECTRONIC STRUCTURE, PROPERTIES, AND THE PERIODIC LAW

HARRY H. SISLER

Head Professor of Chemistry
University of Florida

Arthur and Ruth Sloan
Visiting Professor of Chemistry
Harvard University
Fall 1962–63

REINHOLD PUBLISHING CORPORATION

A subsidiary of Chapman-Reinhold, Inc.
New York   Amsterdam   London

PREFACE

MODERN CHEMISTRY is indeed a complex and multifaceted body of knowledge. So varied are the topics treated that it seems difficult to find a single theme to characterize the field. However, when the developments of the past few decades of chemical research are carefully considered, it becomes apparent that, in *all* areas of chemistry, there has been a strong and continued trend toward the building of a series of theoretical concepts in terms of which it is possible to correlate the results of manifold observations of our physical surroundings with a consistent and dependable picture of the submicroscopic structure of the material world. With each passing year theories of the structures of atoms, molecules, and crystals have become more refined, and use of these concepts to explain experimental results and to predict the results of experiments as yet untried has become more effective. Far from being the purely empirical science of the 19th century, the chemistry of today is growing ever more deductive. It is, therefore, of greatest importance for the student to taste the excitement of the new chemistry early in his study so that as he develops his knowledge of the body of chemical information, he may also breathe the spirit which gives life and unity to this most challenging field of study.

In this small textbook, we shall examine first the manner in which the structures of the various atoms change with atomic number, and hence with position in the Periodic System. We shall, in due course, find in this examination the explanation for the Periodic Law. Having laid this base for

55955

further study, we shall consider some of the more fundamental properties of elements and the manner in which they vary with change in structural parameters. Thus, we shall seek to develop facility in the prediction of these properties in terms of the positions of the atoms in the Periodic System. In so doing we will take a most important step in learning to think as the modern chemist does when he is investigating the frontiers of our ever-broadening knowledge of the chemical world.

As this is being written, I recall the excitement with which I first discovered that the apparently very complex and confusing world of matter and energy is invested with a magnificent order and simplicity. It is my fond hope that this volume may assist the student in experiencing the same intellectual exhilaration.

I would like to express my appreciation to Mrs. Barbara Joan Novogradac and Mrs. Penelope Ansell for typing the manuscript for this volume, to Mr. Robert Beach for preparing the copy for many of the illustrations to be found herein, and to Mrs. Rachel VanderWerf for preparing the index.

I would also like to acknowledge the permission of The Macmillan Company to use several illustrations from the second edition of "College Chemistry—a Systematic Approach" by Sisler, VanderWerf, and Davidson. In addition to those indicated in the appropriate captions, the illustrations of the sodium chloride and carbon dioxide crystals in Table 3.2 were taken from the above-named text.

HARRY H. SISLER

Gainesville, Florida
March, 1963

CONTENTS

CONTENTS

chapter one

ELECTRONIC STRUCTURES OF ATOMS AND THE PERIODIC LAW

MODERN CHEMISTRY is distinguished from the highly empirical science of several decades ago by the rapidly growing ability of the chemist to explain experimental observations in terms of a well-developed and self-consistent theory of the structure of matter in its various forms. *An outstanding example of this has been the successful delineation and explanation of the Periodic Law in terms of the electronic structures of the atoms of the various elements.* This will be our theme. Many chemists believe it to be the most important theme in the whole of chemistry.

If we understand the manner in which the properties of the elements may be correlated with their electronic structures and hence with their positions in the Periodic Chart, we can predict the types of bonds which various atoms form with each other; and knowing the relationship between properties of compounds and the types of chemical bonds which they contain, we can also predict the properties of a multitude of compounds. Of course, our theory of atomic and molecular structure is far from perfect, and there are many limitations on our ability to correlate structure and properties and to predict the properties of previously unknown species. Nevertheless, great progress has been made, and accomplishments of the immediate past most certainly point toward an even more exciting future.

The Nuclear Atom

From the outset we will assume that the reader is familiar with the qualitative aspects of the nuclear theory of atomic structure. In brief review it may be pointed out that the alpha particle scattering experiments of Ernest Rutherford combined with the classical researches of J. J. Thomson on the electronic nature of atoms, and of H. G. J. Moseley on the nuclear charges of atoms, as well as other studies, led to the development of the following principal postulates of atomic structure:

(1) The major portion of the mass of an atom is concentrated in an exceedingly minute, positively charged body at the center of the atom. This positively charged body is called the *nucleus* of the atom.

(2) There are distributed about this central nucleus at relatively large distances from it negatively charged bodies, called electrons, which constitute only a very small fraction of the mass of the atom. These particles have electrical charges equivalent to the smallest quantity of electrical charge ever observed. The electronic mass = 9.107×10^{-28} g. = 0.00005486 atomic mass unit (one atomic mass unit = 1/12th of the weight of the most abundant variety of carbon atoms found in nature). Hence, the electronic charge (1.602×10^{-19} coulomb) is considered to be the unit of electrical charge. Since any atom in its normal state is as a whole electrically neutral, it follows that the number of electrons in any atom must be equal to the number of unit positive charges on its nucleus. Since the nature of these electronic distributions is of great interest to chemists, we shall examine this topic more carefully below.

(3) The radii of atoms are of the order of magnitude of

10^{-8} cm., but the nuclei have radii in the range of 10^{-13} to 10^{-12} cm. It is thus evident that almost all of the mass of an atom is concentrated in an exceedingly small fraction of its volume.

(4) The number of electrons in a neutral atom, which is equal to the number of unit positive charges on its nucleus, is the characteristic which distinguishes all the atoms of a given element. This number, called the atomic number, has the value 1 for hydrogen (the lightest of all the elements), and increases step by step as we proceed through the Periodic System.

(5) Although all atoms of a given element have the same nuclear charge, their nuclear masses may differ considerably. Thus, most hydrogen atoms have masses of approximately 1 a.m.u.; however, a few hydrogen atoms have masses of approximately 2 a.m.u., and a very few have masses that are approximately 3 a.m.u. Atoms having different masses but the same nuclear charge are called *isotopes*. Most elements exist in the form of more than one isotope. Although the nuclear properties of the various isotopes of a given element may vary widely, the ordinary chemical properties treated within the scope of this book are almost the same for the various isotopes of a given element. A possible exception to this statement is H^1, H^2, and H^3, which differ considerably in chemical properties. However, the percentage differences in mass of these isotopes are very great. We shall, therefore, not be greatly concerned with nuclear masses or with the details of nuclear structure. We shall, however, discuss at length the electronic configurations of the various elements and the relationship of these configurations to the chemical properties of the elements.

The Wave Mechanical Theory of the Atom

The study of the spectra of excited atoms has shown that the atoms of the various elements are capable of existing only in certain "allowed," definite energy states (Fig. 1.1)

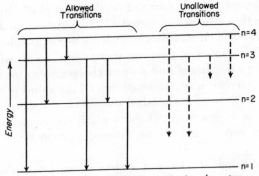

Fig. 1.1. Diagram illustrating quantization of an atom.

and are capable of absorbing or emitting energy only in certain definite quantities, corresponding to the differences in these energy states. Thus, the atom is said to be quantized. Our knowledge of these energy states is derived from the study of the absorption and emission of energy by the atoms as observed in their spectra. Further, the various energy states have been correlated with the electronic configurations of the atoms and have, in fact, provided the principal clue to establishing these configurations. This topic has been discussed in some detail by Prof. G. E. Ryschkewitsch in another volume in this series* to which the reader is referred. However, to provide the immediate basis for the discussion in this volume, it will be necessary to recapitulate and enlarge upon some of the points presented in the above reference.

The presently held theory of the electronic configurations of atoms and molecules is based on the postulate first advanced by the French physicist Louis de Broglie in 1924, that *matter is not only corpuscular in nature, but that each particle possesses*

*Ryschkewitsch, G. E., "Chemical Bonding and the Geometry of Molecules," Chap. 2, Reinhold Publishing Corporation, New York, 1963.

also wave characteristics, having a wave length given by the equation

$$\lambda = h/mv$$

where h = Planck's constant, m = the mass of the particle, and v = the velocity of the particle. This postulate, which has since been amply confirmed by a variety of experimental data, was used by the Austrian physicist Erwin Schrödinger as the basis for a new system of mechanics on which all modern atomic and molecular theory is based. The mathematical details of this new system of mechanics, now known as the *wave mechanics*, are too complex to be appropriate to our present discussion. In simple terms, however, Schrödinger proceeded as follows: Using the classical equation for the motion of standing waves (as, for example, in a vibrating string) and applying de Broglie's postulate that $\lambda = h/mv$, and further specifying that the electron to which the equation refers shall not be at infinity nor shall there be a volume unit at a finite distance from the nucleus in which there is not a finite probability of the electron's existence, Schrödinger derived an equation, called the wave equation, relating an amplitude function for the electron wave (commonly represented by the Greek letter ψ and called a *psi function* or *wave function*) to the kinetic and potential energies of the electron and to the space coordinates in terms of which the system is described. Various wave functions (expressions for ψ) constitute solutions to this equation, and to these allowed wave functions there correspond definite values for the energy of the system. Thus, the various energy states of the atom arise naturally out of the wave equation.

At this point let us consider specifically the significance of the wave function ψ. The intensity (number of photons per unit volume) of a beam of electromagnetic radiation has been shown to be proportional to the square of the amplitude of the electrical vector in the electromagnetic wave. Thus, the density of photons in a beam of light is related to the square of the amplitude function of the light wave.

It seems reasonable to place a similar interpretation on the wave function ψ for "matter waves." Where the wave function refers to a single particle (such as, for example, an electron in an atom), then ψ^2[†] represents the "probability density" corresponding to a given element of volume $dxdydz$. Thus, the probability of finding the electron in a given element of volume $dxdydz$ in space is proportional to the value of $\psi^2dxdydz$ for the particular electron at that point. Another way of looking at the problem is to imagine that the motion of the electron is observed over a period of time. The function ψ^2 will then indicate the time average of the distribution of electrical charge resulting from the motion of the electron. If the function ψ^2 is interpreted in this way, we may think of the electron in terms of an electrically negative charge cloud, the shape of which is determined by the wave function and for which the charge density in any element of volume $dxdydz$ is proportional to $\psi^2dxdydz$.[†] It should be noted that $\psi^2dxdydz$ is *proportional* to the probability of the electron being in the element of volume $dxdydz$, and is not necessarily *equal* to the probability. However, since it can be shown mathematically that if ψ is an acceptable solution to the wave equation then $A\psi$ where A is a constant is also an acceptable solution, we can multiply our wave functions by suitable constants so that $(A\psi)^2dxdydz$ is not only proportional to but is equal to the probability of the electron being in the volume element $dxdydz$. Such a wave function is said to have been normalized. If the electron ex-

[†]In some cases wave functions (ψ) contain the imaginary number i ($= \sqrt{-1}$) and are, therefore, complex numbers. The probability of the electron being in a given element of volume $dxdydz$ must, however, be a real number. Therefore, the product of ψ and its complex conjugate ψ^* is used rather than ψ^2. The product $\psi\psi^*$ will always be real whereas ψ^2 can in certain instances be a complex number. If, for example, ψ is a complex quantity $a + ib$, ψ^* is $a - ib$ and $\psi\psi^*$ is $a^2 + b^2$. If, on the other hand, ψ is a real number, $\psi^* = \psi$ and $\psi\psi^*$ is equivalent to ψ^2.

ists, it is a certainty that it is somewhere in space. This corresponds to a value of one for the probability. Hence, for a normalized wave function the summation of the values of $A^2\psi^2 dxdydz$ over all the volume elements in space will be equal to one. In the language of the calculus this corresponds to the mathematical statement

$$\int A^2\psi^2 dxdydz = 1$$

The above interpretation of the significance of ψ and ψ^2 is not rigorously derivable from any established principles, but is a postulate which depends for its acceptance on the fact that, insofar as it has been possible to test it experimentally, it corresponds to experimental data.

Each solution to the wave equation is characterized by a set of definite values for four numbers, called quantum numbers, commonly represented by the letters n, l, m, and s. These numbers can assume the following values:

$n = 1, 2, 3, 4, 5, \cdots$, any integer
$l = 0, 1, 2, 3, 4, \cdots, n - 1$
$m = +l, (l - 1), (l - 2), \cdots, 0, \cdots, (-l + 2), (-l + 1), -l$
$s = +\frac{1}{2}, -\frac{1}{2}$

An acceptable wave function ψ for an electron in an atom exists for each set of values for these four quantum numbers, and an energy state corresponds to each of these acceptable wave functions. Since each combination of allowed values for these four numbers represents an energy state for an electron in an atom, it will be interesting to review briefly and qualitatively the significance of each of these four quantum numbers.

The number n is known as the *main quantum number.* For single-electron atoms in the absence of a magnetic field, this number determines almost entirely the energy corresponding to a given state. In other words, the energy of an electron in a single-electron atom in the absence of a magnetic field is almost independent of the values of the other three quantum numbers l, m, and s.

The number l is known as the *angular momentum quantum number* and indicates the angular momentum of the electron. The smaller the value of l, the less the angular momentum of the electron, and the higher the probability that it will be near the nucleus; the larger the value of l, the higher the angular momentum, and the higher the probability that the electron will be at distances far from the nucleus. The number l determines the shape of the electron probability distribution (see Figs. 1.7, 1.8 and 1.9).

The quantum number m may be thought of as determining the direction in space relative to an applied magnetic field in which the electron would have the highest probability of being found. Thought of in another way—the movement of an electrical charge (such as the electron in a cyclic path) has a magnetic field associated with it. The *magnetic quantum number m* represents the possible orientations of this magnetic field with respect to an arbitrarily applied magnetic field. It can assume the integral values $-l$, $-l + 1$, $-l + 2$, $\cdots$, 0, $\cdots$, $l - 2$, $l - 1$, l. In the absence of an applied magnetic or electric field, electrons differing only in their values of m, in a given atom have the same energy.

Finally, it appears that not only is there a magnetic field arising out of the orbital motion of the electron, but there is an additional magnetic effect which can only be attributed to the spinning of the electron about an axis. If we presume that the electron possesses a finite volume, such spinning would be equivalent to a circulating electrical charge, and the spinning electron would have a magnetic field associated with it. The *spin quantum number s* has been shown to be capable of assuming two values, viz. $+\frac{1}{2}$ or $-\frac{1}{2}$, corresponding to orientation of the magnetic field associated with the electron spin parallel with or opposed to an applied magnetic field.

Since each set of values for the four quantum numbers corresponds to a solution of the wave equation, characterized by a wave function ψ, and hence, to a possible energy state of the atom, a table of the possible sets of values for these numbers will indicate various possible energy states for an electron in an atom. A list of such sets of values corresponding to $n = 1$, 2, 3, and 4 is provided in Table 1.1.

The Hydrogen Atom According to Wave Mechanics

Reference to Table 1.1 will indicate that for each value of the main quantum number n there are a number of sets of values for the four quantum numbers—two for $n = 1$, eight for $n = 2$, eighteen for $n = 3$, and thirty-two for $n = 4$. However, for single-electron atoms such as hydrogen the energy of the atom depends almost entirely upon the value of n in the absence of a magnetic field, the energy being given by the equation

$$E_n = -\frac{2\pi^2 Z^2 e^4 m}{h^2 n^2}$$

derived by solving the Schrödinger wave equation for a single electron atom, where e = the charge on the electron, m = the mass of the electron, Z = the positive charge on the atomic nucleus and h = Planck's constant.

It should be noted that according to this equation all values of n yield negative values for E_n. This arises from the energy of the electron being defined as the energy absorbed when the electron is brought from a very large distance (infinity) into the electron energy state corresponding to the given value of n. Since in this process energy is actually evolved, E_n is negative. When $n = \infty$, $E_n = 0$, and as the value of n decreases, E_n becomes more negative (Fig. 1.2). In the presence of a magnetic field, however, the energy levels corresponding to each value

TABLE 1.1. Sets of Values for the Four Quantum Numbers (for values of *n* up to *n* = 4)

n	*l*	*m*	*s*	No. of Sets of Values and Notation		
1	0	0	$+\frac{1}{2}$ $-\frac{1}{2}$	2	(1*s*)	2
2	0	0	$+\frac{1}{2}$ $-\frac{1}{2}$	2	(2*s*)	
	1	+1	$+\frac{1}{2}$ $-\frac{1}{2}$			8
		0	$+\frac{1}{2}$ $-\frac{1}{2}$	6	(2*p*)	
		−1	$+\frac{1}{2}$ $-\frac{1}{2}$			
3	0	0	$+\frac{1}{2}$ $-\frac{1}{2}$	2	(3*s*)	
	1	+1	$+\frac{1}{2}$ $-\frac{1}{2}$			
		0	$+\frac{1}{2}$ $-\frac{1}{2}$	6	(3*p*)	
		−1	$+\frac{1}{2}$ $-\frac{1}{2}$			18
	2	+2	$+\frac{1}{2}$ $-\frac{1}{2}$			
		+1	$+\frac{1}{2}$ $-\frac{1}{2}$			
		0	$+\frac{1}{2}$ $-\frac{1}{2}$	10	(3*d*)	
		−1	$+\frac{1}{2}$ $-\frac{1}{2}$			
		−2	$+\frac{1}{2}$ $-\frac{1}{2}$			

TABLE 1.1 (continued)

n	l	m	s	No. of Sets of Values and Notation	
4	0	0	$+\frac{1}{2}$ $-\frac{1}{2}$	2	$(4s)$
	1	+1	$+\frac{1}{2}$ $-\frac{1}{2}$		
		0	$+\frac{1}{2}$ $-\frac{1}{2}$	6	$(4p)$
		−1	$+\frac{1}{2}$ $-\frac{1}{2}$		
	2	+2	$+\frac{1}{2}$ $-\frac{1}{2}$		
		+1	$+\frac{1}{2}$ $-\frac{1}{2}$		
		0	$+\frac{1}{2}$ $-\frac{1}{2}$	10	$(4d)$
		−1	$+\frac{1}{2}$ $-\frac{1}{2}$		
		−2	$+\frac{1}{2}$ $-\frac{1}{2}$		
	3	+3	$+\frac{1}{2}$ $-\frac{1}{2}$		
		+2	$+\frac{1}{2}$ $-\frac{1}{2}$		
		+1	$+\frac{1}{2}$ $-\frac{1}{2}$		
		0	$+\frac{1}{2}$ $-\frac{1}{2}$	14	$(4f)$
		−1	$+\frac{1}{2}$ $-\frac{1}{2}$		
		−2	$+\frac{1}{2}$ $-\frac{1}{2}$		
		−3	$+\frac{1}{2}$ $-\frac{1}{2}$		

The total number of sets of values for $n = 4$ is 32.

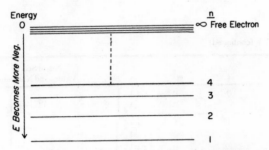

Fig. 1.2. Diagram showing relationship of energy states and values of *n*.

of the main quantum number are split as a result of the various possible interactions of the orbital and spin magnetic fields with the applied magnetic field as indicated by the various values of the quantum numbers *m* and *s*. The result of this splitting of energy levels is that lines in the spectrum of hydrogen (as well as other elements) are split into groups of closely spaced lines. This effect was first observed by Zeeman in 1896 and is commonly known as the Zeeman effect. This effect is illustrated in Fig. 1.3.

The lowest energy state of the hydrogen atom and the state in which we would expect to find an unexcited hydrogen atom is that corresponding to *n* = 1. The wave function ψ, corresponding to this energy state, is of the form which would indicate a high probability of finding the electron near the nucleus. We have seen (p. 6) that the mathematical form of the wave function ψ is such that it can be interpreted in either of two ways. ψ^2 can be viewed as a function which measures the probability of the electron being at a specific point in space; or, if one imagines making an observation of the movement of the electron over a relatively long period of time, ψ^2 would measure the time average of the distribution of electrical charge in space resulting from the motion of the electron. This charge distribution is commonly called the

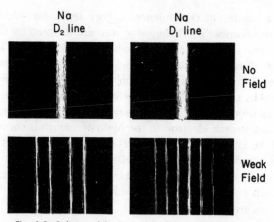

Fig. 1.3. Splitting of the D_2 and D_1 lines in the sodium spectrum by a weak magnetic field—an example of the Zeeman effect.

electron charge cloud corresponding to the particular energy state. The electron charge cloud corresponding to the hydrogen atom in its lowest energy state ($1s$) is illustrated in Fig. 1.4. The same figure shows further how the value of ψ_{1s}^2 varies with distance r from the nucleus.

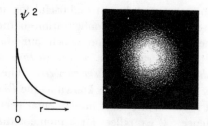

Fig. 1.4. Value of ψ^2 for the hydrogen atom in its lowest energy state (1s) plotted against the radius r; representation of the electronic charge cloud corresponding to this lowest energy state in the hydrogen atom.

As a matter of convenience, energy levels for which the quantum number l has the value zero are denoted by the letter s, those for which l has the value one are denoted by the letter p, those for which l has the value two are denoted by the letter d, and those for which l has the value three are denoted by the letter f. The value of the main quantum number n is used directly in the notation. Thus the lowest energy state for the electron in the hydrogen atom is commonly called the 1s level. An energy level for which $n = 2$ and $l = 1$ would be referred to as a 2p level. Likewise, an energy level for which $n = 3$ and $l = 0$ would be called a 3s level, and one for which $n = 3$ and $l = 2$ would be called a 3d level. These notations are listed in Table 1.1.

Electronic Energy States in Multiple-Electron Atoms

The exact solution of the wave equation for atoms containing more than one electron is a much more difficult task than for the hydrogen atom. Not only must the calculation allow for the attractions between the nucleus and each of the electrons, but also the repulsions between the electrons themselves. It is well beyond the scope of our present discussion to consider the various approaches to a solution of this problem. Rather we shall content ourselves with a semiquantitative approximation, which has proved useful for attaining an understanding of the electronic configurations of the elements.

A fundamental principle upon which our discussion is based states that *in a given atom, no two electrons can have the same set of values for all four quantum numbers*. This principle, first stated by Wolfgang Pauli, is known as the *Pauli Exclusion Principle*, and is one of the most fundamental generalizations in atomic science. If we reflect for a moment that the only thing which distinguishes one electron from another in an atomic system is its particular set of values for the four quantum numbers, we can readily conclude that two electrons which have the same set of values for these numbers would be indistinguishable and hence would be the same electron. Pauli's Exclusion Principle is, therefore, quite reasonable.

In discussing the electronic configurations of the multiple-electron atoms, let us assume that we start with a bare nucleus with a charge of Z^+ units and that we feed electrons into the atoms one at a time until a total of Z electrons have been added, giving a neutral atom. We may take for granted that as long as no excitation energy is supplied, each electron will go into the lowest energy state available to it. One might at first think that all of the electrons would go into the lowest or $1s$ level. However, the Pauli Exclusion Principle stated above limits the number of electrons which can enter each level to the number of combinations of values for the four quantum numbers which correspond to that level. Thus, the number of these combinations determines the electron capacity of each level. The electron capacities of the various levels so determined are listed in Table 1.1. Therefore, as electrons are fed into the atom, the energy states are filled up to their respective capacities in the order of increasing energy. But what is the order of the energies of these various levels? As pointed out above, this problem which was solved precisely for single-electron atoms is much more difficult for the multiple-electron atom. We shall approach the problem by trying to modify the conclusions reached for the single-electron atoms so as to approximate the multiple-electron situation.

As the first electron is brought up to the bare nucleus, the situation is identical with that for a single-electron atom and the energy is given by the previously discussed equation

$$E = -\frac{2\pi^2 Z^2 e^4 m}{h^2 n^2}$$

Now let us make the assumption that each additional electron brought up to the atom remains completely outside of the previously added electrons; in other words, the previously added electrons are considered to be a spherically symmetrical smear of negative charge surrounding the positive nucleus and partially shielding the nucleus from the electron being added (Fig. 1.5). According to this assumption, the energy of

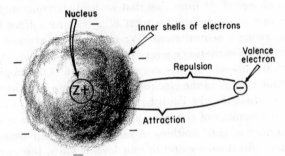

Fig. 1.5. Effect of inner electron shells on a valence electron. (From Sisler, VanderWerf, and Davidson, "College Chemistry—a Systematic Approach," 2nd ed., The Macmillan Company, New York, 1961.)

the electron being added will be given by the equation

$$E = -\frac{2\pi^2(Z - N)^2 e^4 m}{h^2 n^2}$$

where N is the number of previously added electrons. According to this picture, the order of energy levels would be the same as in the hydrogenlike atoms, modified only by the size of the number N.

This, however, does not correspond to the actual situation, for the electrons (as they are added one by one) do not remain completely outside the spherically symmetrical smear of negative charge constituted by the previously added electrons. Rather, the wave function for the electron being added is such that to a greater or lesser extent this electron will penetrate this inner charge cloud. The result of this *penetration effect* is that the added electron will have a lower energy than that given by the above equation. Furthermore, it means that in multiple-electron atoms the order of energy states will be modified by the extent to which electrons in these states penetrate the sphere of negative charge constituted by the inner electrons.

We have already indicated that for a given value of the quantum number n, the probability of finding the electron near the nucleus decreases as the value of the quantum number l increases. Since the energy of the electron is lowered in accordance with the extent to which it penetrates the charge cloud constituted by the inner electrons, we may conclude that for a given value of the main quantum number n the energy of an electron in a given atom increases (i.e., becomes less negative) as the value of l is increased from zero to one to two and on up to $n - 1$. In other words, for a given value of n in a given atom the energy of electrons in an s level is less than if it were in a p level. Likewise a p electron has a lower energy than a d electron, and a d electron less energy than an f electron (assuming in all instances that n has the same value). The result is that in multiple-electron atoms the energy of an electron is not determined solely by the value of the main quantum number n but depends also upon the value of l.

Electron Shells, Subshells, and Orbitals

It is appropriate at this time to consider three terms commonly used in the discussion of electronic configurations of the various elements. The term *electron shell* is used to denote the collection of all sets of values for the four quantum numbers with a given value of n. This means that all of the energy states for which $n = 1$ constitute the first electron shell; those for which $n = 2$ constitute the second electron shell; those for which $n = 3$ the third shell, etc. The maximum electron capacities of these shells as determined by the Pauli Exclusion Principle and listed in Table 1.1 are respectively 2, 8, 18, 32, etc.

The term *electron subshell* is used to denote the collection of sets of values for the four quantum numbers which correspond to the same values for n and l. Thus, the $1s$ energy states for which $n = 1$ and $l = 0$ form the $1s$ subshell, the $2s$ states for which $n = 2$ and $l = 0$ form the $2s$ subshell, the $2p$ states for which $n = 2$ and $l = 1$ form the $2p$ subshell, etc. As indicated in Table 1.1, each s subshell has a capacity of two electrons, each p subshell a capacity of six electrons, each d subshell ten electrons, and each f subshell a capacity of fourteen electrons.

The term *electron orbital* is applied to each pair of sets of values for the four quantum numbers having the same value for n, l, and m and differing only in that for one set $s = +\frac{1}{2}$ and for the other set $s = -\frac{1}{2}$. It is thus apparent that two electrons occupying the same orbital will differ only in having opposite spins. Table 1.1 shows that each s subshell contains one orbital, each p subshell contains three orbitals, each d subshell five orbitals, and each f subshell seven orbitals. The orbitals in a given subshell will, in the absence of an applied magnetic or electric field, generally have equivalent energies.

It should now be clear that the order of energies of the various electronic states in a multiple-electron atom depend not only on the values of the quantum numbers n and l but on the number of electrons in states lower in energy than that of the electron under consideration. It also follows that the order of energy states will be affected by electrons in states higher than that of the electron being considered (this applies in those instances where we are considering an electron other than one in the highest energy state occupied in the atom being discussed). The order of these energy states also depends upon the magnitude of the nuclear charge. Therefore, the delineation of the electronic configurations of the various elements would seem to be an almost impossibly complex task. However, consideration of the problem quickly leads to the conclusion that the essential information needed to build up the electronic configurations of the elements consists only of the relative energies of the subshells in neutral atoms in which the subshell being considered represents the next available subshell into which electrons can go. In other words, to build up the electronic configurations of the elements, we need to know the relative energies of the subshells of the particular neutral atom under consideration. That the relative positions of these subshells in atoms of higher or lower atomic number may differ from this is not pertinent to this immediate problem. Fig. 1.6 gives the order of the energies of the various subshells based on these considerations, and by the utilization of this order of energies we may proceed to build up the electronic configurations of the elements. It should be noted that where two subshells have almost the same energy small variations in atomic parameters which we have not discussed will result in minor variations in the order shown in

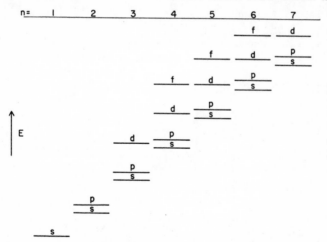

Fig. 1.6. Approximate order of energy states corresponding to various electronic subshells.

Fig. 1.6 and corresponding variations from the systematic order of building up electronic configurations. The electronic configurations of the elements based on the latest information concerning the order of energies for the various electron shells and subshells are given in Table 1.2.

TABLE 1.2   Electronic Configurations of the Elements

Element	At. No.	1s	2s 2p	3s 3p 3d	4s 4p 4d 4f	5s 5p 5d 5f	6s 6p 6d	7s	
H	1	1							
He	2	2							2
Li	3	2	1						
Be	4	2	2						
B	5	2	2 1						
C	6	2	2 2						8
N	7	2	2 3						
O	8	2	2 4						
F	9	2	2 5						
Ne	10	2	2 6						
Na	11	2	2 6	1					
Mg	12	2	2 6	2					
Al	13	2	2 6	2 1					
Si	14	2	2 6	2 2					8
P	15	2	2 6	2 3					
S	16	2	2 6	2 4					
Cl	17	2	2 6	2 5					
Ar	18	2	2 6	2 6					
K	19	2	2 6	2 6	1				
Ca	20	2	2 6	2 6	2				
Sc	21	2	2 6	2 6 1	2				
Ti	22	2	2 6	2 6 2	2				
V	23	2	2 6	2 6 3	2				
Cr	24	2	2 6	2 6 5	1		1st		
Mn	25	2	2 6	2 6 5	2		Transition		
Fe	26	2	2 6	2 6 6	2		Series		
Co	27	2	2 6	2 6 7	2				
Ni	28	2	2 6	2 6 8	2				
Cu	29	2	2 6	2 6 10	1				18
Zn	30	2	2 6	2 6 10	2				
Ga	31	2	2 6	2 6 10	2 1				
Ge	32	2	2 6	2 6 10	2 2				
As	33	2	2 6	2 6 10	2 3				
Se	34	2	2 6	2 6 10	2 4				
Br	35	2	2 6	2 6 10	2 5				
Kr	36	2	2 6	2 6 10	2 6				

No. of Electrons in Each Subshell

TABLE 1.2 (continued)

		1s	2s2p	3s3p 3d	4s4p 4d 4f	5s5p 5d 5f	6s6p 6d 7s	
Rb	37	2	2 6	2 6 10	2 6	1		
Sr	38	2	2 6	2 6 10	2 6	2		
Y	39	2	2 6	2 6 10	2 6 1	2		
Zr	40	2	2 6	2 6 10	2 6 2	2		
Nb	41	2	2 6	2 6 10	2 6 4	1		
Mo	42	2	2 6	2 6 10	2 6 5	1		2nd
Tc	43	2	2 6	2 6 10	2 6 6	1		Transition
Ru	44	2	2 6	2 6 10	2 6 7	1		Series
Rh	45	2	2 6	2 6 10	2 6 8	1		
Pd	46	2	2 6	2 6 10	2 6 10			18
Ag	47	2	2 6	2 6 10	2 6 10	1		
Cd	48	2	2 6	2 6 10	2 6 10	2		
In	49	2	2 6	2 6 10	2 6 10	2 1		
Sn	50	2	2 6	2 6 10	2 6 10	2 2		
Sb	51	2	2 6	2 6 10	2 6 10	2 3		
Te	52	2	2 6	2 6 10	2 6 10	2 4		
I	53	2	2 6	2 6 10	2 6 10	2 5		
Xe	54	2	2 6	2 6 10	2 6 10	2 6		
Cs	55	2	2 6	2 6 10	2 6 10	2 6	1	
Ba	56	2	2 6	2 6 10	2 6 10	2 6	2	
La	57	2	2 6	2 6 10	2 6 10	2 6 1	2	
Ce	58	2	2 6	2 6 10	2 6 10 2	2 6	2	
Pr	59	2	2 6	2 6 10	2 6 10 3	2 6	2	
Nd	60	2	2 6	2 6 10	2 6 10 4	2 6	2	
Pm	61	2	2 6	2 6 10	2 6 10 5	2 6	2	
Sm	62	2	2 6	2 6 10	2 6 10 6	2 6	2	Lanthanides
Eu	63	2	2 6	2 6 10	2 6 10 7	2 6	2	
Gd	64	2	2 6	2 6 10	2 6 10 7	2 6 1	2	
Tb	65	2	2 6	2 6 10	2 6 10 9	2 6	2	3rd
Dy	66	2	2 6	2 6 10	2 6 10 10	2 6	2	Transition
Ho	67	2	2 6	2 6 10	2 6 10 11	2 6	2	Series
Er	68	2	2 6	2 6 10	2 6 10 12	2 6	2	
Tm	69	2	2 6	2 6 10	2 6 10 13	2 6	2	
Yb	70	2	2 6	2 6 10	2 6 10 14	2 6	2	32
Lu	71	2	2 6	2 6 10	2 6 10 14	2 6 1	2	
Hf	72	2	2 6	2 6 10	2 6 10 14	2 6 2	2	
Ta	73	2	2 6	2 6 10	2 6 10 14	2 6 3	2	
W	74	2	2 6	2 6 10	2 6 10 14	2 6 4	2	
Re	75	2	2 6	2 6 10	2 6 10 14	2 6 5	2	
Os	76	2	2 6	2 6 10	2 6 10 14	2 6 6	2	
Ir	77	2	2 6	2 6 10	2 6 10 14	2 6 9		
Pt	78	2	2 6	2 6 10	2 6 10 14	2 6 9	1	
Au	79	2	2 6	2 6 10	2 6 10 14	2 6 10	1	
Hg	80	2	2 6	2 6 10	2 6 10 14	2 6 10	2	
Tl	81	2	2 6	2 6 10	2 6 10 14	2 6 10	2 1	

		3s	3p	3d	4s	4p	4d	4f	5s	5p	5d	5f	6s	6p	6d	7s	
Pb		2	6	10	2	6	10	14	2	6	10		2	2			
Bi	83	2	6	10	2	6	10	14	2	6	10		2	3			
Po	84	2	6	10	2	6	10	14	2	6	10		2	4			
At	85	2	6	10	2	6	10	14	2	6	10		2	5			
Rn	86	2	6	10	2	6	10	14	2	6	10		2	6			
Fr	87	2	6	10	2	6	10	14	2	6	10		2	6		1	
Ra	88	2	6	10	2	6	10	14	2	6	10		2	6		2	
Ac	89	2	6	10	2	6	10	14	2	6	10		2	6	1	2	⎫
Th	90	2	6	10	2	6	10	14	2	6	10		2	6	2	2	
Pa	91	2	6	10	2	6	10	14	2	6	10	2	2	6	1	2	
U	92	2	6	10	2	6	10	14	2	6	10	3	2	6	1	2	
Np	93	2	6	10	2	6	10	14	2	6	10	5	2	6		2	Actinides
Pu	94	2	6	10	2	6	10	14	2	6	10	6	2	6		2	
Am	95	2	6	10	2	6	10	14	2	6	10	7	2	6		2	
Cm	96	2	6	10	2	6	10	14	2	6	10	7	2	6	1	2	
Bk	97	2	6	10	2	6	10	14	2	6	10	8	2	6	1	2	
Cf	98	2	6	10	2	6	10	14	2	6	10	10	2	6		2	⎭

Incomplete 4th Transition Series

Note that a series of elements in which a *d* subshell is being built up is known as a *transition series*. Note further that the series of elements in which the 4*f* subshell is being filled is called the *lanthanide* series* and the series in which the 5*f* subshell is being filled is called *actinide* series.* The electronic configurations of elements 99, 100, 101, 102, and 103 have not yet been established and these elements are, therefore, omitted from Table 1.2.

Electronic Configurations and Magnetic Characteristics of Atoms

The values of the magnetic quantum numbers *m* and *s* corresponding to the energy states occupied by electrons in a particular atom play an important role in determining the magnetic characteristics of substances containing that atom. Let us, for example, consider the situation that exists when a *p*

*For a discussion of the chemistry of these interesting elements, see Moeller, T., "The Chemistry of the Lanthanides," Reinhold Publishing Corporation, New York, 1963.

subshell contains three electrons. Reference to Table 1.1 indicates that each *p* subshell contains three orbitals. There is more than one way in which the three electrons can be placed in the orbitals of the *p* subshell. Two of the electrons can go into one of the orbitals, in which case they will have opposite spins, and the third electron can go into a second orbital. Another possibility is that one electron can go into each orbital, in which case none of the spins need be paired. A study of atomic spectra reveals that in the process of pairing two electrons in an orbital, energy is absorbed and, therefore, electrons in a given subshell do not pair off unless the number of such electrons in the given subshell in comparison to the number of orbitals in the subshell require them to pair, and further that the spins of all the electrons in the subshell will be parallel until the operation of the *Pauli Exclusion Principle* forces the electron to begin pairing. An empirical rule commonly known as *Hund's Rule* states that *in a given atom, so long as the Pauli Exclusion Principle permits, electrons in the same subshell* (i.e., with the same values of *n* and *l*) *will occupy orbitals with different values of m and their spins will not pair up.* The order of filling of the orbitals in *s*, *p*, *d*, and *f* subshells and the pairing of electron spins is shown in Table 1.3. The normal arrangement of electrons and spins corresponding to any number of electrons in any type of subshell can be obtained by referring to this table.

Let us now recall that there is associated with each electron a magnetic moment resulting from its spin (p. 8). Depending upon whether its spin quantum number is $+\frac{1}{2}$ or $-\frac{1}{2}$, the magnetic moment of the electron can be oriented parallel with an applied magnetic field or opposed to the applied magnetic field. Since *paired* electrons have different spins (p. 18), their magnetic moments will oppose each other and cancel. However, the *unpaired* electrons in a given subshell all have parallel spins (as shown in Table 1.3) and will cause the atom, molecule, or other chemical species to which they belong to have a

TABLE 1.3. Orbital and Spin Arrangements for the Various Types of Subshells by Hund's Rule*

s	p	d	f
↑ s¹	↑ _ _ p¹	↑ _ _ _ _ d¹	↑ _ _ _ _ _ _ f¹
↑↓ s²	↑ ↑ _ p²	↑ ↑ _ _ _ d²	↑ ↑ _ _ _ _ _ f²
	↑ ↑ ↑ p³	↑ ↑ ↑ _ _ d³	↑ ↑ ↑ _ _ _ _ f³
	↑↓ ↑ ↑ p⁴	↑ ↑ ↑ ↑ _ d⁴	↑ ↑ ↑ ↑ _ _ _ f⁴
	↑↓ ↑↓ ↑ p⁵	↑ ↑ ↑ ↑ ↑ d⁵	↑ ↑ ↑ ↑ ↑ _ _ f⁵
	↑↓ ↑↓ ↑↓ p⁶	↑↓ ↑ ↑ ↑ ↑ d⁶	↑ ↑ ↑ ↑ ↑ ↑ _ f⁶
		↑↓ ↑↓ ↑ ↑ ↑ d⁷	↑ ↑ ↑ ↑ ↑ ↑ ↑ f⁷
		↑↓ ↑↓ ↑↓ ↑ ↑ d⁸	↑↓ ↑ ↑ ↑ ↑ ↑ ↑ f⁸
		↑↓ ↑↓ ↑↓ ↑↓ ↑ d⁹	↑↓ ↑↓ ↑ ↑ ↑ ↑ ↑ f⁹
		↑↓ ↑↓ ↑↓ ↑↓ ↑↓ d¹⁰	↑↓ ↑↓ ↑↓ ↑ ↑ ↑ ↑ f¹⁰
			↑↓ ↑↓ ↑↓ ↑↓ ↑ ↑ ↑ f¹¹
			↑↓ ↑↓ ↑↓ ↑↓ ↑↓ ↑ ↑ f¹²
			↑↓ ↑↓ ↑↓ ↑↓ ↑↓ ↑↓ ↑ f¹³
			↑↓ ↑↓ ↑↓ ↑↓ ↑↓ ↑↓ ↑↓ f¹⁴

*The arrows ↑ and ↓ represent the two directions of electron spin.

net magnetic moment which can be quantitatively related to the number of such unpaired electrons. Such substances are attracted by an applied magnetic field and tend to be drawn into the field; they are known as *paramagnetic* substances.

In addition to the magnetic moment contributed by the spin of unpaired electrons, one must, in order to evaluate the magnetic properties associated with various chemical species, consider the magnetic moment associated with the orbital motion of the electrons. This contribution to the magnetic moment is related to the magnetic quantum number m (p. 8).

The net magnetic moments of paramagnetic substances are the resultants of the spin and the orbital contributions. Just as a pair of electrons has no resultant spin magnetic moment, a filled or a half-filled electron subshell has no net orbital magnetic moment (the sum of the values for the magnetic quantum number m for all the electrons in a filled or half-filled subshell is zero). This may be checked by referring to the data in Table 1.1. Furthermore, the process of forming chemical bonds usually destroys any orbital magnetic moment for outer electron subshells.

Substances which have no net magnetic moment are slightly repelled by an applied magnetic field and are known as *diamagnetic* substances. In most paramagnetic substances, the major contribution to the magnetic moment is from unpaired electrons. Hence, Hund's rule as expressed in the data in Table 1.3 is most useful in relating magnetic moments to electronic configurations.

Spatial Aspects of Electronic Energy States

We have seen (p. 5) that for wave functions which are used to describe atomic systems there exists a finite probability that an electron in any energy state will be at almost any particular point in space. We cannot, therefore, draw any sort of spatial figure which will completely encompass the electronic charge distribution corresponding to an electron in a particular energy state. We can, however, draw spatial contour diagrams which will represent the region in space which will include a specific fraction of the electronic charge, let us say 95%.

For electrons in s subshells we find that the probability distribution (or the time average of electron charge density) is independent of direction in space and varies only with distance from the nucleus. The distribution is, therefore, spherically symmetrical in form and is of the type illustrated in Fig. 1.7.

The probability distribution for p orbitals is, however, strongly dependent on direction. The electron charge cloud for an electron in a p orbital is of the form indicated in

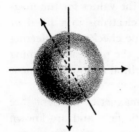

Fig. 1.7. Charge distribution for an electron in an *s* orbital. (From Sisler, Vander-Werf, and Davidson, "College Chemistry—a Systematic Approach," 2nd ed., The Macmillan Company, New York, 1961.)

Fig. 1.8. As we have seen, there are three orbitals in each *p* subshell, corresponding to the three different values of the quantum number *m*. These three orbitals differ from one another only in their spatial orientation. They may be described in terms of the three axes in the rectangular coordinate system, one orbital being oriented along each of the *x*, *y*, and *z* axes as shown in Fig. 1.8. The three orbitals are commonly denoted as p_x, p_y, and p_z orbitals.

The probability distributions for electrons in *d* orbitals are more complex in form than are those for *p* electrons. Each *d* subshell contains five orbitals. The wave functions for these orbitals are of such a nature that the probability distributions

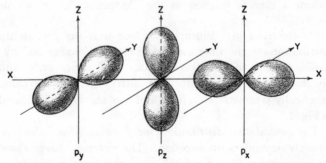

Fig. 1.8. Charge distributions for electron in p_y, p_z, and p_x orbitals.

(or electron charge clouds) for the five orbitals have the forms indicated in Fig. 1.9. The notations indicated in the figure are given to these orbitals because of their respective relationships to the x, y, and z axes in the rectangular coordinate system. It should be noted that in a free atom, and in the

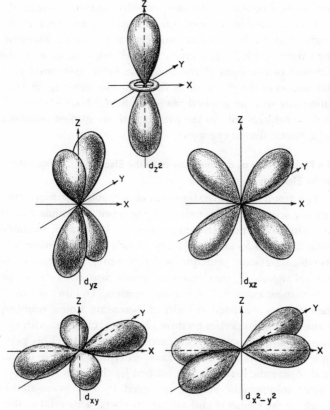

Fig. 1.9. Charge distributions for electrons in d_{z^2}, d_{yz}, d_{xz}, d_{xy}, and $d_{x^2-y^2}$ orbitals.

absence of an applied magnetic or electric field, the various orbitals in a given subshell correspond to the same energy. However, in a nonuniform electrical field such as is obtained when the atom forms a part of a molecule or crystal, the various orbitals in a given subshell because of their different spatial characteristics interact with the field in different ways and therefore correspond to different energies. For this reason, it is frequently necessary to distinguish between the various orbitals in the electron subshells of an atom in the study of molecular structure and crystal structure. Likewise, the various orbitals in a given subshell will, because of the different orientations of the magnetic fields associated with the motion of the electrons in the respective orbitals, interact differently with an applied magnetic field. Hence, electrons in these orbitals will, in the presence of an applied magnetic field, have different energies.

The Periodic Law as a Consequence of the Electronic Configurations of the Elements

As a result of the investigations of a number of nineteenth century scientists, culminating in the work of Lothar Meyer and Dmitri Mendeleeff announced in 1869, and modified some four decades later by Henry Moseley, the following profoundly significant principle was discovered: *The physical and chemical properties of the elements are periodic functions of the charges on their atomic nuclei, i.e., their atomic numbers.* In other words, if the elements are listed in order of increasing atomic number, many of their properties go through cyclical changes, with elements of similar properties recurring at intervals. This principle is known as the Periodic Law. A typical example of this kind of periodic variation is furnished by the relation between atomic volume (the volume occupied by one gram-atomic weight of the element) and atomic number. This relationship is illustrated in Fig. 1.10. A consideration of this figure along with the periodic variations of a number of other physi-

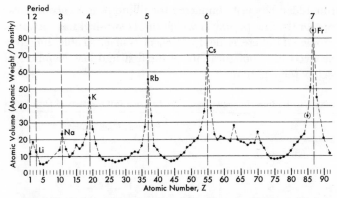

Fig. 1.10. Variation of Atomic Volumes of the Elements with Atomic Number. (From Sisler, VanderWerf, and Davidson, "College Chemistry—a Systematic Approach," 2nd ed., The Macmillan Company, New York, 1961.)

cal and chemical properties of the elements with their atomic numbers indicates that the sequence of the elements arranged in order of increasing atomic number may be naturally divided into seven periods—the first containing two elements, the second and third having eight elements, the fourth and fifth eighteen elements, and the sixth thirty-two elements. The last period is incomplete.

For many years after the first statement of the Periodic Law, no theoretical explanation for the law was available and it was used simply as an empirical principle. However, with the development of the electronic theory of atomic structure, it became possible to understand the theoretical basis for the Periodic Law. If we examine the table of electronic configurations given in Table 1.2 and correlate these configurations with the compositions of the various periods of elements as exemplified in Fig. 1.10, we see that the beginning of each of the periods corresponds to an element in which a new *s* subshell is begun and that the last element in each complete period has an electronic configuration in which the last electron added has just completed the filling of a p subshell, except for the first period in which the $1s$ subshell has just been completed—there is no $1p$ level, of course. Table 1.4 gives the electronic configurations of the first and last members of each of these periods.

TABLE 1.4. Electronic Configurations of the First and Last Members of Each Period

Period	First Element	Electronic Configuration						
1	H	1						
2	Li	2	1					
3	Na	2	2,6	1				
4	K	2	2,6	2,6	1			
5	Rb	2	2,6	2,6,10	2,6	1		
6	Cs	2	2,6	2,6,10	2,6,10	2,6	1	
7	Fr	2	2,6	2,6,10	2,6,10,14	2,6,10	2,6	1

Last Element	Electronic Configuration					
He	2					
Ne	2	2,6				
Ar	2	2,6	2,6			
Kr	2	2,6	2,6,10	2,6		
Xe	2	2,6	2,6,10	2,6,10	2,6	
Rn	2	2,6	2,6,10	2,6,10,14	2,6,10	2,6

We immediately recognize that the first elements of these periods collectively form what is commonly known as the alkali metal family (hydrogen is not commonly included in this family), a group of elements characterized by close similarity in chemical and physical properties. The last elements in the periods constitute the group of elements until recently known as the inert gases, which have a relatively low degree of reactivity toward other elements (see also p. 112). Other groups of elements which occupy analogous positions in the various periods have electronic configurations that are similar with respect to their outer electron shells. Thus, *the periodic recur-*

rence of elements with similar physical and chemical properties, when the elements are listed in order of increasing atomic number, results directly from the periodic recurrence of similar electronic configurations in the outer shells of the respective atoms.

Periodic Tables

Since the first statement of the Periodic Law by Meyer and Mendeleeff nearly a century ago, the periodic relationships between the order of the elements and their physical and chemical properties have been expressed in a variety of tables, in which the elements of similar properties appear in a horizontal row or, more commonly, a vertical column. The groups of similar elements thus delineated have come to be known as periodic *families*. The form of these periodic tables has varied considerably and some exceedingly bizarre charts have been constructed. However, in recent years the development of understanding concerning the relationship of electronic configurations of the atoms and the Periodic Law has resulted in the wide acceptance of periodic charts of the form shown in Fig. 1.11. In this chart each horizontal row corresponds to a single period. In the sixth and seventh periods the lanthanide and actinide elements are omitted from the body of the table in order to make it less cumbersome. These elements are placed in separate rows at the bottom of the chart. Since the lanthanides resemble lanthanum so closely and since the actinides bear a similar resemblance to actinium, this arrangement causes no great loss in the utility of the chart.

A form of periodic chart which seeks to correlate even more closely the filling of the various electronic subshells with the Periodic Law is shown in Fig. 1.12.

Characteristics and Usefulness of the Periodic Law

Considered in the light of its historical significance and, more importantly, its present usefulness, the discovery of the

1a	2a	3b	4b	5b	6b	7b	8b			1b	2b	3a	4a	5a	6a	7a	0
1 H																1 H	2 He
3 Li	4 Be											5 B	6 C	7 N	8 O	9 F	10 Ne
11 Na	12 Mg											13 Al	14 Si	15 P	16 S	17 Cl	18 Ar
19 K	20 Ca	21 Sc	22 Ti	23 V	24 Cr	25 Mn	26 Fe	27 Co	28 Ni	29 Cu	30 Zn	31 Ga	32 Ge	33 As	34 Se	35 Br	36 Kr
37 Rb	38 Sr	39 Y	40 Zr	41 Nb	42 Mo	43 Tc	44 Ru	45 Rh	46 Pd	47 Ag	48 Cd	49 In	50 Sn	51 Sb	52 Te	53 I	54 Xe
55 Cs	56 Ba	57-71	72 Hf	73 Ta	74 W	75 Re	76 Os	77 Ir	78 Pt	79 Au	80 Hg	81 Tl	82 Pb	83 Bi	84 Po	85 At	86 Rn
87 Fr	88 Ra	89-103															

Lanthanides	57 La	58 Ce	59 Pr	60 Nd	61 Pm	62 Sm	63 Eu	64 Gd	65 Tb	66 Dy	67 Ho	68 Er	69 Tm	70 Yb	71 Lu
Actinides	89 Ac	90 Th	91 Pa	92 U	93 Np	94 Pu	95 Am	96 Cm	97 Bk	98 Cf	99 Es	100 Fm	101 Md	102	103 Lw

Fig. 1.11. A modern periodic chart. (From Sisler, VanderWerf, and Davidson, "College Chemistry—a Systematic Approach," 2nd ed., The Macmillan Company, New York, 1961.)

Periodic Law (leading as it did to the development of Periodic Charts) constitutes one of the most singularly important events in the history of chemical science. Almost every chemist makes extensive and continued use of the Periodic Law. The following chapters of this book will be devoted to showing how the various properties of chemical substances may be correlated with the positions of the various elements in the Periodic Chart.

It will be useful at this point to list some of the more elementary characteristics of the Periodic Chart:

(1) Elements in a given vertical column in the chart have similar chemical and physical properties.

(2) There is usually a regular gradation in many physical and chemical properties of the elements in a given family with increase in atomic number.

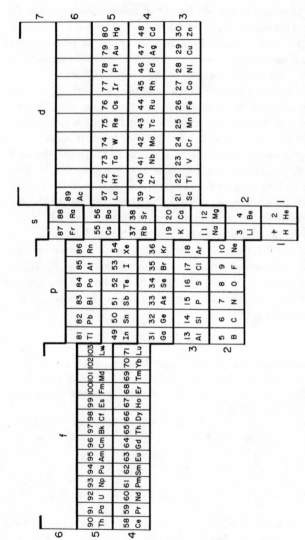

Fig. 1.12. Another modern periodic chart (Redrawn from Sheehan, "Physical Chemistry," Allyn and Bacon, Boston, 1961.)

(3) Elements in a given family in most instances have the same maximum oxidation number.

(4) There is commonly a regular trend in physical and chemical properties as we pass from element to element in a given horizontal row (period) in the Periodic Chart.

The Periodic Chart makes it possible for chemists to study the chemistry of the elements as families rather than as individuals and thus greatly simplifies the task of acquiring and maintaining a working knowledge of chemical facts.   The Chart provides a stimulus and a guide in chemical research, constantly suggesting as it does new experiments to be tried and providing a basis for critically evaluating and checking information already obtained.   The chart has led to the discovery of new elements and in several instances has shown that the claimed discovery of a new element is false.   The very existence of the Periodic Law as an empirical principle provided a tremendous stimulus to the development of our knowledge of atomic structure and greatly accelerated the growth of our understanding of the relationship of the structure and the properties of matter.

Suggested Readings

Cartmell, E., and Fowles, G. W. A., "Valency and Molecular Structure," 2nd ed., pp. 3–61, Academic Press, Inc., New York, 1961.

Cotton, F. A., and Wilkinson, G., "Advanced Inorganic Chemistry," pp. 3–31, Interscience Publishers, New York, 1962.

Day, M. C., and Selbin, J., "Theoretical Inorganic Chemistry," pp. 1–95, Reinhold Publishing Corporation, New York, 1962.

Pauling, L., "The Nature of the Chemical Bond," 3rd ed., pp. 28–63, Cornell University Press, Ithaca, New York, 1960.

Ryschkewitsch, G., "Chemical Bonding and the Geometry of Molecules," Chaps. 1 and 2, Reinhold Publishing Corporation, New York, 1963.

Sanderson, R. T., "Chemical Periodicity," pp. 1–15, Reinhold Publishing Corporation, New York, 1960.

Sisler, H., VanderWerf, C., and Davidson, A., "General Chemistry —A Systematic Approach," 2nd ed., pp. 115–177, The Macmillan Company, New York, 1959.

Sisler, H., VanderWerf, C., and Davidson, A., "College Chemistry —a Systematic Approach," 2nd ed., pp. 100–122, The Macmillan Company, New York, 1961.

chapter two ——————————————————

CHEMICAL BONDING AS A FUNCTION OF ATTRACTION FOR ELECTRONS

ONE OF THE MOST important aspects of the periodic variation of the properties of the elements lies in the ability of the chemist to predict the types of bonds which two specific kinds of atoms will form in terms of certain atomic parameters which in turn may be correlated with the positions of the elements in the Periodic Chart.

The types of chemical bonds formed by atoms in their various compounds have been treated in detail in another volume of Selected Topics in Modern Chemistry.* We shall survey this topic only briefly to provide a basis for subsequent discussions.

Types of Chemical Bonds

Bonding forces between atoms which are of sufficient magnitude to be considered "chemical bonds" can be roughly divided into two classes. One of these classes, known as *ionic* or *electrovalent* bonds, involves the transfer of electrons from one of the reacting species to another, and produces a sub-

*Ryschkewitsch, G. E., "Chemical Bonding and the Geometry of Molecules," Selected Topics in Modern Chemistry, Reinhold Publishing Corporation, New York, 1963.

stance which consists of an array of positively and negatively charged ions. This type of substance depends for its stability largely upon the electrostatic or coulombic energy of interaction between the positive and negative charges on the ions. As is indicated in the discussion which follows, the number of electrons transferred depends on the electronic configurations of the atoms of the reacting elements.

In the other principal class of bonds, known as *covalent* bonds, two or more atoms are held together in a single molecule or complex ion through the mechanism of sharing one or more pairs of electrons between the two atoms. In order for a bond of this sort to form, there must be available on each of the bonding atoms an electronic orbital of suitable geometry to overlap in space with an electronic orbital on the other atom to form a bonding orbital (sometimes called a *molecular orbital*) in which the shared pair of electrons may reside. The energy liberated in this process is called the *bond energy*. Thus, in the fluorine molecule (F_2) a p orbital from one fluorine atom overlaps with a p orbital from the other fluorine atom and a pair of electrons is shared between the two atoms thus forming part of the electronic configuration of both (Fig. 2.1).

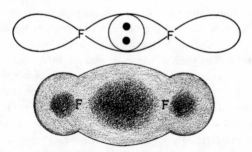

Fig. 2.1. Electron cloud resulting from the formation of an electron-pair bond involving the overlap of two p orbitals in the F_2 molecule.

The strength of the covalent bond is roughly related to the extent to which the appropriate orbitals on the two bonding atoms can overlap in space. Thus, p orbitals generally form stronger bonds than s orbitals because the spatial characteristics of p and s orbitals are such (Figs. 1.7 and 1.8) that p orbitals extend out into space from the nucleus along an axis, whereas s orbitals are concentrated in a spherical configuration relatively near the nucleus.

Furthermore, since the three orbitals in a given p subshell are oriented along x, y, and z axes that are at right angles to each other, we should expect atoms that form two or three bonds by the use of p orbitals to have bonds oriented at right angles to each other.

However, there are many instances in which the geometry of molecules does not correspond to that which would be predicted on the basis of the orientation of s, p, d, and f atomic orbitals in space. Thus, in the compound monosilane, SiH_4, in which the silicon atom uses one s orbital and three p orbitals to form four covalent bonds, it might be predicted that the result would be three strong bonds oriented at right angles to each other, plus a weaker bond which would be nondirectional in character. Actually, studies of the monosilane molecule show that all four Si—H bonds are equivalent in strength and are directed toward the corners of a regular tetrahedron, giving bond angles slightly greater than 109° (Fig. 2.2). Experimental results such as these, as well as theoretical studies, have served to emphasize that in the process of bond formation the s, p, d, and f orbitals which exist in the free atoms may undergo modification and rearrangement. The wave functions which describe the electronic orbitals in the uncombined atoms are converted by appropriate wave mechanical calculations to new wave functions which describe new orbitals in terms of which the covalent bond formation may be interpreted. This mathematical process is sometimes called *hy-*

bridization and the resulting orbitals called *hybrid orbitals*. Thus, an atom with one s and three p orbitals in forming four covalent bonds yield through the hybridization process four equivalent sp^3 hybrid orbitals which extend in space toward the corners of a regular tetrahedron. Table 2.1 lists the types of hybrid orbitals commonly encountered.

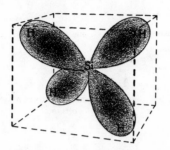

Fig. 2.2. Use of sp^3 hybrid orbitals in the formation of four equivalent bonds by the silicon atom in the SiH_4 molecule.

It should be noted that the existence of electrons in hybrid electron orbitals represents higher energy states for uncombined atoms than occurs with ordinary electronic configurations in which electrons reside in s, p, d, or f orbitals. Thus, for an uncombined silicon atom the electron configuration $1s^2 2s^2 2p^6 (3s 3p^3)^4$ corresponds to a higher energy than the electronic configuration $1s^2 s^2 2p^6 3s^2 3p^2$ which is the ground state. However, because of the superior bond-forming characteristics of the sp^3 hybrid orbitals, the increase in energy necessary to promote electrons in the silicon atom from the $3s^2 3p^2$ configuration to the $(3s 3p^3)^4$ configuration is more than counterbalanced in silicon compound by the decrease in energy resulting from the stronger bonds which sp^3 hybrid orbitals form as compared with s and p orbitals.

TABLE 2.1. Some Common Types of Hybrid Bond Orbitals

Hybrid Bond Orbitals	Geometrical Configurations	Formed From:	Examples
sp	LINEAR	one s and one p orbital	$Ag(NH_3)_2{}^+$, $HgCl_2$
sp^2	TRIGONAL PLANAR	one s and two p orbitals	BF_3, $NO_3{}^-$
sp^3	TETRAHEDRAL	one s and three p orbitals	CH_4, SiF_4, $SO_4{}^{2-}$, $NH_4{}^+$
dsp^2	SQUARE PLANAR	one d, one s, and two p orbitals	$Pt(NH_3)_2Cl_2$, $Ni(CN)_4{}^{2-}$
d^2sp^3 or sp^3d^2	OCTAHEDRAL	two d, one s, and three p orbitals	$Cr(NH_3)_6{}^{3+}$, $SiF_6{}^{2-}$, $Fe(CN)_6{}^{3-}$

There are many varieties of ionic and covalent bonding. However, most chemical bonds may be discussed in terms of these two general types.

Bond Type and the Attraction of Atoms for Electrons

In the prediction of the properties of a substance it is important to be able to make a reasonable judgment as to the type of chemical bonds that will be characteristic of the particular substance. Let us now consider how one might reasonably make such a judgment. Suppose that we are considering the reaction of two types of atoms which we shall represent by the symbols X and Y. Let us further assume that each of these atoms contains at least one electron in its outer shell. Now we ask the question "What kind of bond will these two atoms form?" It can readily be shown that if a stable ionic bond is to be formed between the two atoms, or, more accurately, if groups of the two atoms are to react to form a stable ionic crystal, the two types of atoms must differ considerably in their attraction for electrons. We must carefully note at this point that in the formation of an ionic compound, the driving force of the reaction is not a spontaneous tendency for one kind of atom to lose electrons and for another kind of atom to gain electrons. The formation of a positive ion from a neutral atom under the conditions of chemical reaction is never a spontaneous process, and in only a relatively few instances does the formation of negative ions from neutral atoms take place spontaneously (p. 42). Rather, the principal driving force for the formation of an ionic substance is the energy released when widely separated positive and negative ions come together under the influence of electrostatic attraction and form an ionic crystal. This can be illustrated by the formation of potassium chloride from metallic potassium and gaseous chlorine.

Taking advantage of the principle that the energy evolved or absorbed in a given chemical reaction is always the same regardless of the path by which the reaction occurs, we may arbitrarily choose a path for the reaction that is convenient for us to discuss, knowing that the over-all energy change associated with that path will be the same as for all other possible paths. We shall, therefore, assume that the reaction between potassium metal and gaseous chlorine takes place by the following path:

$$K_{(solid)} \xrightarrow{(1)} K_{(gas)} \xrightarrow{(3)} K^+_{(gas)}$$

$$\xrightarrow{(5)} K^+Cl^-_{(solid)}$$

$$\tfrac{1}{2}Cl_{2\,(gas)} \xrightarrow{(2)} Cl_{(gas)} \xrightarrow{(4)} Cl^-_{(gas)}$$

The energy of the reaction $K_{(solid)} + \tfrac{1}{2}Cl_{2(gas)} \rightarrow K^+Cl^-_{(solid)}$ will be equal to the sum of the energies corresponding to steps (1), (2), (3), (4), and (5). Step (1) corresponds to the sublimation of the solid metal, step (2) to the dissociation of the Cl_2 molecules into free atoms, step (3) to the loss of an electron by each metal atom, step (4) to the taking up of an electron by each of the Cl atoms to form Cl^- ions. Steps (1), (2), and (3) all involve the absorption of energy and the energy evolved in step (4) is far from sufficient to overcome the energy deficit set up in steps (1), (2), and (3). Therefore, up to this point the reaction is endoenergetic and, hence, is nonspontaneous.* However, in step (5) the widely separated K^+ and Cl^- ions condense under the attractive force of the electrostatic interaction of their opposite electrical charges, and in this process a sufficiently large amount of energy is evolved to more than balance the energy absorbed in other steps of the reaction. The total reaction is, therefore, exoenergetic and, hence, spontaneous.* If, however, in a reaction of this sort the atom losing electrons requires the absorption of very large amounts of energy to remove its valence electrons, and

*Spontaneous chemical reactions are those which occur with a decrease in the *free energy* of the system. Hence, the above statement that *exoenergetic* reactions are spontaneous and endoenergetic reactions are nonspontaneous is strictly true only if the terms *exoenergetic* and *endoenergetic* refer to changes in free energy. *Exothermic* and *endothermic* refer to changes in heat content or *enthalpy* of the system. These two terms do not correlate precisely with the terms spontaneous and nonspontaneous. A number of endothermic processes such as, for example, the melting of ice at 25°C., are spontaneous. The if the atom gaining electrons releases very little energy or actually absorbs energy (as is true in some cases where one electron per atom is acquired and in all cases where more than one electron per atom is taken up), it may be that the energy evolved in the condensation of the positive and negative ions to form a crystalline solid will be insufficient to overcome the energy deficit. Unless the energy deficit is overcome, the reaction to form an ionic compound will not occur. We, therefore, return to our original statement, that in order for atoms X and Y to react to form a stable ionic crystal, the atoms X and Y must differ considerably in their attraction for electrons. *Ionic substances, therefore, are formed by the reaction of elements whose atoms have only a small attraction for the electrons in their outer shell with elements which have a large attraction for electrons in their outer shell.* Similarly, the number of electrons lost per atom of one element and the number gained per atom of the other element in the process of ionic bond formation is limited by energy considerations to those numbers for which the energy deficit produced in the formation of the positive and negative ions will not outweigh the energy gained from the formation of the ionic crystal lattice.

As we shall see below (pp. 52 and 59), the difficulty in removing electrons from atoms and in adding electrons, increases with the respective removal or addition of each successive electron. Therefore, one almost never encounters

---

relationship between change in enthalpy and change in free energy is given by the equation

$$\Delta F = \Delta H - T\Delta S$$

where ΔF is the increase in free energy, ΔH is the increase in enthalpy, and ΔS is the increase in entropy of the system. Entropy is related to the degree of randomness in a system and the term $T\Delta S$ measures the tendency for the particles in a system to become disordered. Since this tendency becomes greater at higher temperatures, the term contains the absolute temperature as a factor.

truly ionic crystals which contain positive or negative ions having charges greater than three units.

Now consider the case where atoms X and Y have the same attraction for electrons. Clearly, under these conditions there can be no electron transfer between X and Y. Hence since atoms X and Y fail to differ in their attraction for electrons, the reaction between these two atoms will not result in the formation of an ionic crystal. Instead, there will be formed a molecule in which the atoms X and Y are held together by covalent bonds in which pairs of electrons are shared equally by the two atoms. The electron cloud constituted by this pair of electrons will be concentrated symmetrically in the space between the two atoms. Since under these circumstances the electrical charges in the resulting molecule are symmetrically distributed, this type of covalent bond is said to be *nonpolar*. This precise condition of the equal sharing of a pair of electrons can, of course, occur only when X and Y are atoms of the same element, for no two elements have atoms with exactly equal attractions for electrons.*

A much more common situation is that in which atoms X and Y differ in their attraction for electrons, but insufficiently so to fulfill the requirements for the formation of an ionic crystal. In this case, atoms X and Y combine by sharing electrons to form a covalent bond, but the negative charge cloud constituted by the pair of shared electrons is shifted toward the atom with the greater attraction for electrons, causing that atom to have an excess of negative charge and the atom of lesser attraction for electrons a corresponding excess of

*Note that when the reacting atoms do not differ greatly in their attraction for electrons, but all the atoms concerned have *low* attractions for electrons a special type of electron sharing which leads to the formation of metallic crystals occurs. The unique characteristics of metallic crystals will be discussed in Chapter 3 (p. 92). The data concerning the formation of metallic crystals do not conflict with the point of view of the present discussion.

positive charge. The bond formed in this case is called a *polar* covalent bond. The magnitude of the polarity will depend upon the magnitude of the difference in attraction that atoms X and Y have for electrons. As this difference in attraction increases, the polarity of the bond increases, until finally the difference in attraction for electrons becomes sufficient to allow complete electron transfer and an ionic crystal is obtained. Thus, we see that the formation of ionic bonds and of nonpolar covalent bonds represent extreme situations and that the intermediate case is the formation of polar covalent bonds. This relationship is summarized in the scheme below.

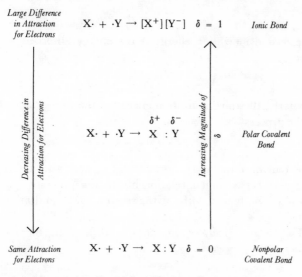

It should now be clear that the prediction of the type of bond which two atoms will form requires a knowledge of the relative attractions for outer electrons exhibited by the two atoms. It is important, therefore, that we understand how attraction for electrons varies from atom to atom in the Periodic Chart.

Measures of Attraction for Electrons

There are three different quantities which are commonly used as measures of the attraction which atoms have for electrons in their outer shells. They are (a) the ionization energy, (b) the electron affinity, and (c) the electronegativity.

The *ionization energy* of an element is the energy *absorbed* in the process of removing an electron from an atom of the element when the element is in the form of a dilute, atomic gas. The first ionization energy is the minimum energy required to remove the least tightly bound electron from the atom; i.e., it is the energy absorbed in the process

$$A_{(gas)} \longrightarrow A^+_{(gas)} + e^-_{(gas)}$$

The second ionization energy is the energy absorbed in the process

$$A^+_{(gas)} \longrightarrow A^{2+}_{(gas)} + e^-_{(gas)}$$

Similarly, the third ionization energy is the energy absorbed in the process

$$A^{2+}_{(gas)} \longrightarrow A^{3+}_{(gas)} + e^-_{(gas)}$$

The fourth, fifth, sixth, seventh, . . . , and nth ionization energies bear a similar relationship to the processes for removal of the fourth, fifth, sixth, seventh, . . . , and nth electrons.

The *electron affinity* of an atom is defined as the energy *evolved* in the process

$$A_{(gas)} + e^-_{(gas)} \longrightarrow A^-_{(gas)}$$

Similarly, the second electron affinity would correspond to the energy evolved in the process

$$A^-_{(gas)} + e^-_{(gas)} \longrightarrow A^{2-}_{(gas)}$$

and the third electron affinity corresponds to the energy absorbed in the process

$$A^{2-}_{(gas)} + e^{-}_{(gas)} \longrightarrow A^{3-}_{(gas)}$$

and so on.

The *electronegativity* of an atom may be qualitatively defined as a measure of the attraction of that atom for a pair of electrons being shared in a covalent bond with another atom. R. S. Mulliken has proposed that the electronegativity of an atom should be the average of its ionization energy (which measures the tendency of the atom to hold on to its own electrons) and its electron affinity (which measures the tendency of the atom to attract additional electrons). Several different methods for the estimation of the relative electronegativities of the elements have been used; these various methods yield, in general, similar results.

Let us now consider the variation of ionization energy, electron affinity, and electronegativity with changes in atomic structure and with position of the respective elements in the Periodic Chart.

Factors Determining the Ionization Energies of the Elements

The ionization energy is a direct measure of the energy state of the least tightly held electron in an atom or ion, except that the energy of the electron and the ionization energy have opposite signs. This difference in sign arises from the way in which these energies are defined. The *energy of an electron in a particular energy state in an atom* is defined as the energy absorbed when the electron is brought from a very large distance from the nucleus (precisely, infinity) to the electron orbital which corresponds to that energy state for that electron. Since in this process energy is actually evolved, the sign of the energy is negative (see also p. 9 and Fig. 1.2). On the other hand, the *ionization energy* is defined as the energy absorbed in removing the electron from the energy state in which it is residing to an infinite (practically, very large) distance from the nucleus. Since energy is absorbed in this process, ionization energies carry a positive sign.

We may assume that appropriate solutions to the wave mechanical equation for an atom will yield values for the various ionization energies. However, without carrying out these calculations but simply by considering qualitatively the effect of certain appropriate parameters we are able to predict trends in ionization energies as a function of position of the element in the Periodic Chart. The parameters which may be considered to determine the ionization energies of a given element are:

(a) *The nuclear charge.* It is clear that apart from other effects the effect of increasing nuclear charge is to increase the ionization energy for any given electron in the atom.

(b) *The main quantum number n of the energy state in which the electron resides.* Let us assume that factors other than the value of n remain constant. Then, since the term n^2 appears in the denominator of the equation describing the energy of a particular electronic state (see p. 16), as n increases the energy of the electron will increase, i.e. become less negative; therefore, the ionization energy will decrease, i.e. become less positive.

(c) *The shielding effect of inner electrons.* As was pointed out in the last chapter, in multiple-electron atoms an electron in the outer electron shell is repelled by the electronic charge cloud constituted by the electrons in inner shells, thus partially counter-balancing the attraction of the positively charged nucleus for the electron in the outer shell (see Fig. 1.5). Thus, if other factors remain constant, an increase in the number of inner electrons will tend to decrease the ionization energy of an outer electron.

The shielding effect of inner electrons depends, however, not only on their number, but also on their electronic energy states, i.e. the subshells in which they reside. We have already seen (p. 16) that the shielding effect of inner electrons is not 100% efficient because the valence electrons penetrate to a greater or lesser extent within the electron cloud constituted by the inner electrons. The point is that the degree of penetration depends not only on the quantum number l of the valence electron, which effect has already been discussed (p. 17) and which is considered under (d) below, but also on the quantum number l of the outermost of the inner electron subshells. For a given value of n the electron cloud is concentrated most closely to the nucleus when $l = 0$, i.e. in an s orbital. As l successively takes on the values 1, 2, 3, ..., $n - 1$, the electron cloud changes so as to decrease step by step the negative charge distribution near the nucleus. Hence, the shielding efficiency of inner electrons decreases in the order $s > p > d > f$. In other words, the extent to which a valence electron will penetrate an s subshell is less than for a p subshell, which in turn is penetrated less than a d subshell or f subshell; i.e., tendency to be penetrated by an outer electron increases for inner electrons in the order $s < p < d < f$. A factor which enhances this effect is the fact that complete s subshells contain only two electrons, complete p subshells six, filled d subshells ten, and f subshells 14 electrons. Thus, penetration of a filled d subshell reduces the shielding effectiveness of 10 electrons, whereas penetration of a filled p subshell affects the shielding effect of only six inner electrons. The combination of these two factors results in electrons which are immediately underlain by a full d subshell being much more strongly attracted than electrons immediately underlain by a full p subshell.*

(d) *The angular momentum quantum number l of the energy state in which the electron resides.* We have already seen (p. 17) that,

---

* This accounts in part for the much lower reactivity of copper, silver, and gold than of potassium, rubidium, and cesium, respectively.

because of the penetration effect, the energy of an outer electron in a multiple-electron atom depends not only on the main quantum number n but also depends on the value of the angular momentum quantum number l. The amount of penetration of the inner-electron shells by an outer electron decreases for a given value of n as the value of l for the outer electron increases from 0 to $n - 1$ because in this order the probability of finding the electron relatively near the nucleus decreases. Thus, the ionization energy will decrease as the electron moves from the s subshell to the p subshell to the d subshell to the f subshell, provided the effects of other factors remain constant. This is equivalent to our earlier statement (p. 17) that for a given electron shell, energies corresponding to the various subshells increase in the order $s < p < d < f$.

An examination of the energies of the valence electrons in the single-valence-electron atoms lithium, sodium, potassium, rubidium, cesium, copper, silver, and gold will serve to illustrate the effects discussed under (c) and (d). If there is no penetration by the single valence electron into the charge cloud composed of the inner electrons, the valence electron will experience 100% effective shielding by these inner electrons. For this situation, we may write the following expression for the energy:

$$E = -2\pi^2(\mathcal{Z} - \mathcal{N})^2 e^4 m / h^2 n^2 \qquad \text{(p. 16)}$$

For atoms with but a single valence electron, $\mathcal{N} = \mathcal{Z} - 1$ and $\mathcal{Z} - \mathcal{N} = 1$. Hence, the above equation may be written for single-valence-electron atoms as follows:

$$E = -2\pi^2 e^4 m / h^2 n^2$$

But, of course, there is penetration, and this equation does not yield the correct values for the energies as experimentally determined. However, we may write the empirical equation

$$E = -2\pi^2 e^4 m / h^2 (n^*)^2$$

where n^* is an empirically determined number which when inserted into the equation gives the correct value for the energy. Comparison of the values of n and n^* gives a measure of the effect of penetration. The greater the value of $n - n^*$, the greater the penetration effect. Table 2.2 gives n^* and n

TABLE 2.2 Values of n^* (n in parentheses)

	s	p	d	f
Li	1.59(2)	1.96(2)	3.00(3)	4.00(4)
Na	1.63(3)	2.12(3)	2.99(3)	4.00(4)
K	1.77(4)	2.23(4)	2.85(3)	3.99(4)
Rb	1.80(5)	2.28(5)	2.77(4)	3.99(4)
Cs	1.87(6)	2.33(6)	2.55(5)	3.98(4)
Cu	1.33(4)	1.86(4)	2.98(4)	4.00(4)
Ag	1.34(5)	1.87(5)	2.98(5)	3.99(4)
Au	1.21(6)	1.72(6)	2.98(6)	

values for the lowest s-, p-, d-, and f-states of the alkali metals and copper, silver, and gold.[†] The data in Table 2.2 strikingly illustrate how much greater the penetration effect is for a valence electron in a deeply penetrating s-orbital than for a less deeply penetrating p-orbital. These data also show clearly that the penetration effect is much greater for heavy atoms than for light atoms which have fewer electrons in inner shells for the valence electrons to penetrate. Finally, the data show how much greater the effect is for atoms in which the first penetrable subshell contains 10 electrons (i.e. is a d-subshell as e.g. in the copper atom) than when the first penetrable subshell has only six electrons (i.e. is a p-subshell as e.g. in the potassium atom).

(e) *The net charge on the atom or ion.* Leaving all other considerations aside, we find that the ionization energy of an atom or ion will depend upon its net charge. Thus if the ef-

[†]Rice, O. K., "Electronic Structure and Chemical Binding," p. 96, McGraw-Hill, New York, 1940.

fects of all other factors are assumed to be constant, then the ionization energy of a neutral atom will be less than that of a singly charged positive ion and the ionization energy for a singly charged positive ion will be less than that of a doubly charged positive ion. In other words, for a given atom, the ionization energies increase in the order 1st < 2nd < 3rd < 4th < 5th < 6th < 7th < etc.

The methods sometimes used to determine ionization energies are such as to make it convenient to express these energies in electron-volts. An electron-volt is defined as the energy acquired by an electron or other particle carrying a unit electrical charge when it falls through a potential difference of one volt. Sometimes these data when so expressed are called ionization potentials. Ionization energies may, of course, be expressed in any energy unit, such as e.g. kilocalories per mole.

Trends in Ionization Energies of the Elements

Ionization energy data for the elements of the first three periods of the Periodic Chart are listed in Table 2.3.

The data for the *first* ionization energies of the elements of the first three periods of the Periodic Chart are listed in Table 2.4. Let us consider how the factors discussed above may be used in rationalizing these data. We note in the first place that there is a large increase in first ionization energy as we pass from hydrogen to helium. This is readily explained by the fact that the charge on the helium nucleus is double that on the hydrogen nucleus; moreover, since the first electron is in the same subshell as the second electron and hence similarly distributed with respect to the nucleus, the first electron does not greatly shield the second electron. As we come to lithium, however, there is a large drop in first ionization energy because the main quantum number of the least tightly bound electron is now 2 and the increase in nuclear charge is largely counterbalanced by the strong shielding effect that the two $1s$ electrons exert on the $2s$ electron. With beryllium,

TABLE 2.3. Ionization Energies for the Elements in the First Three Periods

| | Electron Configuration | | | Period | Ionization Energies (Electron-Volts) | | | | | | | |
	1 (s)	2 (s p)	3 (s p)		1st	2nd	3rd	4th	5th	6th	7th	8th
H	1			Period I	13.6							
He	2				24.6	54.4						
Li	2	1		Period II	5.4	75.6	122.4					
Be	2	2			9.3	18.2	153.9	217.7				
B	2	2,1			8.3	25.1	37.9	259.3	340.1			
C	2	2,2			11.3	24.4	47.9	64.5	392.0	489.8		
N	2	2,3			14.5	29.6	47.4	77.5	97.9	551.9	666.8	
O	2	2,4			13.6	35.1	54.9	77.4	113.9	138.1	739.1	871.1
F	2	2,5			17.4	35.0	62.6	87.2	114.2	157.1	185.1	953.6
Ne	2	2,6			21.6	41.1	64.0	97.2	126.4	157.9		
Na	2	2,6	1	Period III	5.1	47.3	71.7	98.9	138.6	172.4	208.4	264.2
Mg	2	2,6	2		7.6	15.0	80.1	109.3	141.2	186.9	225.3	266.0
Al	2	2,6	2,1		6.0	18.8	28.4	120.0	153.8	190.4	241.9	285.1
Si	2	2,6	2,2		8.1	16.3	33.4	45.1	166.7	205.1	246.4	303.9
P	2	2,6	2,3		11.0	19.7	30.2	51.4	65.0	220.4	263.3	309.3
S	2	2,6	2,4		10.4	23.4	35.0	47.3	72.5	88.0	281.0	328.8
Cl	2	2,6	2,5		13.0	23.8	39.9	53.5	67.8	96.7	114.3	348.3
Ar	2	2,6	2,6		15.8	27.6	40.9	59.8	75.0	91.3	124.0	143.5

however, the first ionization energy once again becomes greater. This arises from the increase in nuclear charge, since the second $2s$ electron is not effectively shielded by the first $2s$ electron.

TABLE 2.4. First Ionization Energies (Electron-Volts)

H 13.6							He 24.6
Li 5.4	Be 9.3	B 8.3	C 11.3	N 14.5	O 13.6	F 17.4	Ne 21.6
Na 5.1	Mg 7.6	Al 6.0	Si 8.1	P 11.0	S 10.4	Cl 13.0	Ar 15.8

There is a slight decrease in first ionization energy when we come to boron because the increase in nuclear charge is outweighed by the fact that in the boron atom the least tightly bound electron is a $2s$ rather than a $2s$ electron. As we pass from boron to carbon to nitrogen, the increase in first ionization energy is associated with the increase in nuclear charge and the fact that electrons in a given subshell are not effectively shielded from the nucleus by other electrons in the same subshell. With the element oxygen ionization energy decreases slightly. This may be correlated with the slight increase in stability that is associated with any half-filled or completely filled subshell. In the nitrogen atom the $2p$ subshell is half-filled; and the next $2p$ electron is held somewhat less tightly than would otherwise be the case. From oxygen to fluorine to neon, we observe the normal increase in first ionization energy produced by increasing nuclear charge unbalanced by an effective increase in shielding or change in quantum numbers.

With the element sodium there is once again a large decrease in first ionization energy which can be attributed to the fact the main quantum number of the least tightly bound electron is now 3 instead of 2. The change in first ionization energies throughout the elements of the third period parallel closely the corresponding changes in the elements of the second period.

The first ionization energies of all the elements are plotted as a function of atomic number in Fig. 2.3. This plot indicates that in the fourth, fifth, and sixth periods, the trends in first ionization energies are roughly analogous to those in the earlier periods except for the series of closely spaced ionization energies corresponding to the transition elements and lanthanides.

The first ionization energies of the elements in several families of the Periodic Chart are listed in Table 2.5. These illustrate

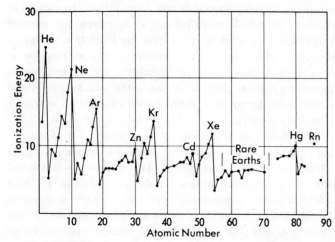

Fig. 2.3. Variation with atomic number of the first ionization energies of the elements. (From Sisler, VanderWerf, and Davidson, "College Chemistry— a Systematic Approach," 2nd ed., The Macmillan Company, New York, 1961.)

vertical trends in first ionization energy within the Periodic Chart.

TABLE 2.5. First Ionization Energies (Electron-Volts)

The Alkali Metal Family		The Alkaline Earth Metal Family		The Oxygen Family		The Halogens	
Li	5.4	Be	9.3	O	13.6	F	17.4
Na	5.1	Mg	7.6	S	10.4	Cl	13.0
K	4.3	Ca	6.1	Se	9.8	Br	11.8
Rb	4.2	Sr	5.7	Te	9.0	I	10.4
Cs	3.9	Ba	5.2				
		Ra	5.3				

If we consider the elements in a given vertical column (or family) of the Periodic Chart, we find that their ionization energies are affected by three factors, viz. the change in nuclear charge, the change in the value of the quantum number n, and the change in the number of inner electrons. As we pass, for example in the alkali metal family, from lithium to sodium to potassium to rubidium to cesium to francium the nuclear charge increases, tending to increase the ionization energy in that order. However, there is simultaneously an increase in the value of the main quantum number n and an increase in the number of inner electrons to shield the least tightly bound electron from the nucleus. Both of these effects tend to reduce the ionization energy.

The resultant effect of all three of these factors is, in general, to cause a gradual decrease in ionization energy as we go from the lighter to the heavier elements in the family. An exception to this trend occurs with elements of atomic number greater than 71. With an element of atomic number 72 or greater, the nuclear charge is 32 units greater than that of the next lightest member of the respective family. This very large difference in nuclear charge reverses or at least greatly reduces the trend toward lower ionization energies. Thus, francium has a slightly higher ionization energy than cesium and radium has a higher ionization energy than barium. As one goes from lighter to heavier elements in the various periodic families, there are certain other minor exceptions to the trend toward lower ionization energies, but these are relatively unimportant.

Finally, consider the successive ionization energies associated with the removal of one, two, three, four, ..., and n electrons from a given atom. We have already noted that in any series of this sort ionization energy increases with the removal of each successive electron. If we examine the data in Table 2.3 more carefully, we see that as each subshell is depleted and the first electron is withdrawn from the next lower subshell, the jump in ionization energy is large. When a whole electron shell has been depleted and the first electron is drawn from the next lower shell, there is a very large increase in ionization energy. This is to be expected, for the main quantum number has been decreased by one unit. The values of the successive ionization energies of a given atom, therefore, delineate clearly the number of valence electrons, and determine the number of electrons which may be lost in ionic bonding.

In summary, it may be stated that *the principal trend in ionization energies from left to right in the Periodic Chart is a general increase*, and that *from top to bottom in a given column in the chart the trend is a general decrease in ionization energies, except for the elements with atomic numbers greater than 71.* Minor variations from these trends have been noted above.

Trends in Electron Affinities of the Elements

Electron affinities, like ionization energies, are commonly expressed in electron-volts or kilocalories per mole. The form of the definition of electron affinities (p. 46) is such that if the acquiring of an electron by an atom takes place with the evolution of energy the electron affinity will have a positive sign. The factors which determine the magnitude and sign of electron affinities are, in general, similar to those we have used to explain the ionization energies of the elements. In fact, the electron affinity of a neutral atom may be thought of simply as the negative of the ionization energy of the singly charged negative ion of that atom. Unfortunately, electron affinity data are available for only a few of the elements. Such data are listed in Table 2.6.

The electron affinity data which are available indicate the expected general trend toward larger electron affinities as one proceeds from left to right in the Periodic Chart. Exceptions are found in the cases of beryllium and magnesium, nitrogen and phosphorus, and the inert gases. The atoms of beryllium and magnesium have completely filled *s* subshells, and an electron being added to one of these atoms would face the necessity of residing in a subshell of considerably higher energy. Thus, electron affinities of zero for beryllium and magnesium are to be expected.

TABLE 2.6.   Electron Affinities (Electron-Volts)

(a) *For one electron:*							
H							He
0.7							0
Li	Be	B	C	N	O	F	Ne
0.54	0	0.3	1.13	0.2	1.48	3.62	0
Na	Mg	Al	Si	P	S	Cl	Ag
0.74	0	0.4	1.90	0.80	2.07	3.82	0
					Se	Br	Kr
					—	3.54	0
(b) *For two electrons:*						I	Xe
O	S	Se				3.24	0
−7.3	−3.4	−4.2					Rn
							0

This is even more emphatically the case with the elements of the helium family where the outer electron shells of atoms contain filled *s* and *p* subshells, and the incoming electron must go into an electron shell having a larger value for the main quantum number *n*. The atoms of nitrogen and phosphorus each have half-filled *p* subshells, the extra stability of which has already been noted (p. 54); and it is not surprising that the electron affinity corresponding to the addition of one electron beyond this condition of relative stability is less than would otherwise be expected.

One would also expect that electron affinities would decrease from lighter to heavier elements in a given column of the Periodic Chart. This trend is observed for the sequence chlorine, bromine, and iodine; also the affinities for two electrons for the elements sulfur and selenium are in the right order. However, each member of the series lithium, beryllium, boron, carbon, nitrogen, oxygen, and fluorine has a lower electron affinity than the next heavier member of its respective periodic family. This rather unexpected effect has tentatively been correlated with the repulsion between the electrons already present in the atom and the electron being added. It is reasoned that this effect would be unusually large with the relatively small atoms in this series.

Second (and higher order) electron affinities are all negative in sign because of the repulsion between the electron being added and the already negatively charged atom.

Trends in the Electronegativities of the Elements

General acceptance of the concept of electronegativity as a measure of the relative ability of an atom in a molecule to attract electrons to itself is almost universal in the chemical world. However, the method of measuring the electronegativity of an element and the correlation of this quantity with other atomic parameters have been, and still are, the objects of considerable speculation, discussion, and argument—unfortunately, not always entirely amiable. Part of the difficulty is that, in contrast to ionization energies and electron affinities which may be related to isolated atoms in the gaseous state, electronegativities pertain to atoms which are combined with other atoms to form molecules. Therefore, the electronegativity of an element is not only a function of the structure of the atom of the particular element concerned, but also depends to a large degree on the number and kind of atoms with which it is combined. Since most elements exhibit a great variety of chemical combinations, the electronegativity of an element is not a fixed and unchangeable constant. One should be prepared, for example, to find that the electronegativity of the phosphorus atom relative to the chlorine atom is different in the compound $C_6H_5PCl_2$ than it is in the compound $OPCl_3$.

Since there is so little agreement among chemists as to the best method for determining electronegativities, and since the values obtained by the various methods are, in general, similar, we shall not discuss the details of the various methods. Suffice it to say that virtually all the methods are adjusted to yield numbers representing relative electronegativities in the range of from slightly less than one to approximately four, and they are based more or less closely on properties which can be related to the degree of polarity of the covalent bonds that a particular element forms with other elements.

As a typical example of a scale of electronegativities, Table 2.7 lists the values derived by Pauling* from a comparison of the energies of bonds A—B with the energies for the bonds A—A and B—B.

TABLE 2.7.   Scale of Electronegativities of the Elements (by Pauling)

Li 1.0	Be 1.5					H 2.1						B 2.0	C 2.5	N 3.0	O 3.5	F 4.0
Na 0.9	Mg 1.2											Al 1.5	Si 1.8	P 2.1	S 2.5	Cl 3.0
K 0.8	Ca 1.0	Sc 1.3	Ti 1.5	V 1.6	Cr 1.6	Mn 1.5	Fe 1.8	Co 1.8	Ni 1.8	Cu 1.9	Zn 1.6	Ga 1.6	Ge 1.8	As 2.0	Se 2.4	Br 2.8
Rb 0.8	Sr 1.0	Y 1.2	Zr 1.4	Nb 1.6	Mo 1.8	Tc 1.9	Ru 2.2	Rh 2.2	Pd 2.2	Ag 1.9	Cd 1.7	In 1.7	Sn 1.8	Sb 1.9	Te 2.1	I 2.5
Cs 0.7	Ba 0.9	La-Lu 1.1-1.2	Hf 1.3	Ta 1.5	W 1.7	Re 1.9	Os 2.2	Ir 2.2	Pt 2.2	Au 2.4	Hg 1.9	Tl 1.8	Pb 1.8	Bi 1.9	Po 2.0	At 2.2
Fr 0.7	Ra 0.9	Ac 1.1	Th 1.3	Pa 1.5	U 1.7	Np-Lw 1.3										

The data in Table 2.7 show that as we pass from element to element in a horizontal row across the Periodic Chart the general trend is toward increasing electronegativity, and as we pass from the lighter to the heavier elements in a given vertical column, the trend is generally a slow decrease in electronegativity.   Minor exceptions to these trends are to be found, particularly among the transition elements.   These trends are in agreement with the trends we have noted in other measures of the attractions of atoms for their outer electrons, viz. ionization energies and electron affinities.

*Pauling, L., "The Nature of the Chemical Bond," 3rd ed., p. 93, Cornell University Press, Ithaca, N. Y., 1960.

Classification of the Elements—Metals and Nonmetals

The attraction of atoms for electrons in their outer shells is conveniently used as a basis for dividing the elements of the periodic system into two classes. Those elements whose atoms have a relatively small attraction for their outer electrons as indicated by relatively small ionization energies, electron affinities, and electronegativities, are known as *metals;* whereas the elements having a relatively large attraction for outer electrons as indicated by relatively high ionization energies, electron affinities, and electronegativities, are known as *nonmetals*. The trends in ionization energies, in electron affinities, and in electronegativities all indicate that attraction for outer electrons generally increases from left to right in a given row across the Periodic Chart and that attraction for outer electrons decreases from lighter to heavier elements in a given vertical column in the Periodic Chart. The trends in metallic and nonmetallic properties reflect these trends. Thus, we find the most active nonmetals in the upper right corner of the Periodic Chart (ignoring the helium family) and the most active metals in the lower left corner of the chart. These relationships are illustrated in Fig. 2.4.

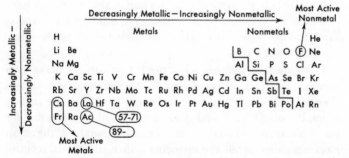

Fig. 2.4. Variation of metallic and nonmetallic properties with position in the periodic system. (From Sisler, VanderWerf and Davidson, " College Chemistry—a Systematic Approach," The Macmillan Company, New York, 1961.)

The Use of the Periodic Chart in Predicting Bond Type

Having established the fact that the type of bond which will be formed between two elements depends upon the relative attraction of the elements for outer electrons, and having further established the trends in the magnitude of this attraction in the Periodic Chart, we may now discuss the prediction of bond type from the positions of the elements in the Periodic Chart.

Let us consider, for example, the formation of a chemical bond between selenium and bromine in the compound $SeBr_2$. We see immediately that since selenium and bromine are adjacent elements in the Periodic Chart, we should expect their ionization energies and electronegativities to be similar and that each of these elements may be expected to be a nonmetal of moderate activity. It is clear that for these atoms attraction for electrons would not be sufficiently different to allow the formation of an ionic bond; rather a covalent bond of relatively low polarity will be formed.

If, on the other hand, we are interested in the reaction of strontium and bromine to form $SrBr_2$, it is apparent from their positions in the Periodic Chart that the two elements concerned differ considerably in their attraction for electrons. Strontium is in the active metal section of the Periodic Chart, and bromine is an active nonmetal. We should expect, therefore, that the bonds formed between these two elements would be of the ionic type.

Using these principles, what prediction can we make concerning the type of bond which the elements silicon and fluorine will form? Silicon is an element located in the middle of the Periodic Chart, and is intermediate in its attraction for outer electrons. Fluorine, on the other hand, is the most electronegative of all the elements and is the most reactive nonmetal. However, in view of the relatively large amount of energy required to remove all four valence electrons from the silicon atom, it would not be expected that SiF_4 would be an ionic compound. Rather, we would expect that the Si—F bonds in this compound would be covalent with a marked degree of polarity.

There are, of course, many instances where it is indeed difficult to make a prediction in which a high degree of confidence can be placed. There are also situations where the simplified approach we are using will lead to incorrect conclusions. The principles presented here are reliable in most instances, however, and experience in dealing with questions of this sort will develop an awareness of the type of situation where the application of these generalized principles may lead to invalid conclusions.

The Formation of Metallic Phases

A situation of particular interest arises when the atoms of both reacting elements are characterized by having a relatively low attraction for outer electrons, in other words, when both of the reacting elements are metals. Since there is relatively little difference in the attraction of the two elements for outer electrons, the principles developed above would lead to the conclusion that the bonds between the two types of atoms would be of the covalent type. As a matter of fact, considered in very broad terms, the conclusion may be considered to be correct. However, if we consider the bonds which exist in the substances formed by the interaction of two or more metallic elements to be covalent in character, they represent a very special type of covalent bonding, indeed. Therefore, in the next chapter where attention is given to the properties which various types of bonds confer on chemical substances, special attention will be given to the characteristics of metallic phases, and to the nature of the bonds which hold their atoms together. One of the characteristics of the products of the interactions of two or more metals is that in many instances a given pair of metals form several different products whose

TABLE 2.8. Transition from Intermetallic Phases to Ionic Compounds in the Binary Compounds of Magnesium

Increasing difference in attraction for outer electrons →						
		Al_3Mg_2 $Al_{12}Mg_{17}$	Mg_2Si	Mg_3P_2	MgS	$MgCl_2$
Mg_2Cu $MgCu_2$	MgZn $MgZn_2$ Mg_2Zn_{11}	Mg_5Ga_2 Mg_2Ga MgGa $MgGa_2$	Mg_2Ge	Mg_3As_2	MgSe	$MgBr_2$
Mg_3Ag MgAg	Mg_3Cd $MgCd_3$	Mg_5In_2 Mg_2In MgIn $MgIn_3$	Mg_2Sn	Mg_3Sb_2	MgTe	MgI_2
Mg_3Au Mg_5Au_2 Mg_2Au MgAu	Mg_3Hg Mg_5Hg_2 Mg_2Hg Mg_5Hg_3 MgHg $MgHg_2$	Mg_5Tl_2 Mg_2Tl MgTl	Mg_2Pb	Mg_3Bi_2		

Intermetallic Phases   ?   Ionic Compounds

compositions do not correspond to the typical valences of the elements concerned. Table 2.8 illustrates what happens when a metal forms compounds with a series of elements of increasing attraction for electrons. In this table are listed the formulas of the compounds that the metal magnesium forms with the elements of a series of families in the Periodic Chart, arranged in the order in which the families appear in the chart, i.e., in the order of increasing attraction of their atoms for outer electrons. As the table indicates, as the attraction for outer electrons on the part of the element with which the magnesium is reacting increases, the nature of the resulting compound shifts from the intermetallic type of phase toward the typical ionic compound.

Table 2.9 gives similar information for binary compounds of lithium and sodium with elements of increasing attraction for outer electrons. Such data as these provide excellent examples of the relationship of bond type to the difference in the attraction for outer electrons of the atoms forming the bond.

TABLE 2.9. Transition from Intermetallic Phases to Ionic Compounds in the Binary Compounds of Lithium and Sodium

			Increasing difference in attraction for outer electrons				
		$LiZn$, Li_2Zn_3, $LiZn_2$, Li_2Zn_5, $LiZn_4$	$LiGa$		Li_3As	Li_2Se	$LiBr$
Li	Li_3Ag, $LiAg$	Li_3Cd, $LiCd$, $LiCd_3$	$LiIn$	Li_4Sn, Li_7Sn_2, Li_5Sn_2, Li_2Sn, $LiSn$, $LiSn_2$	Li_3Sb	Li_2Te	LiI
		Li_6Hg, Li_3Hg, Li_2Hg, $LiHg$, $LiHg_2$, $LiHg_3$	Li_4Tl, Li_3Tl, Li_5Tl_2, Li_2Tl, $LiTl$	Li_4Pb, Li_7Pb_2, Li_3Pb, Li_5Pb_2, $LiPb$	Li_3Bi		
		$NaZn_4$, $NaZn_{13}$		$NaGe$	Na_3As	Na_2Se	$NaBr$
Na		$NaCd_2$, $NaCd_5$	$NaIn$	$Na_{15}Sn_4$, Na_2Sn, Na_4Sn_3, $NaSn$, $NaSn_2$	Na_3Sb	Na_2Te	NaI
	Na_2Au, $NaAu_2$	Na_3Hg, Na_5Hg_2, Na_3Hg_2, $NaHg$, Na_7Hg_8, $NaHg_2$, $NaHg_4$	Na_6Tl, Na_2Tl, $NaTl$	$Na_{15}Pb_4$, Na_5Pb_2, Na_2Pb, $NaPb$, $NaPb_3$			

| *Intermetallic Phases* | *Ionic Compounds* |

Suggested Readings

Cartmell, E., and Fowles, G. W. A., "Valency and Molecular Structure," 2nd ed., pp. 65–138, Academic Press, New York, 1961.

Cotton, F. A., and Wilkinson, G., "Advanced Inorganic Chemistry," pp. 36–84, Interscience Publishers, New York, 1962.

Day, M. C., and Selbin, J., "Theoretical Inorganic Chemistry," pp. 96–178, Reinhold Publishing Corporation, New York, 1962.

Pauling, L., "The Nature of the Chemical Bond," 3rd ed., pp. 3–27, 65–142, Cornell University Press, Ithaca, N. Y., 1960.

Ryschkewitsch, G. E., "Chemical Bonding and the Geometry of Molecules," Selected Topics in Modern Chemistry, Reinhold Publishing Corporation, New York, 1963.

Sanderson, R. T., "Chemical Periodicity," pp. 16–36, Reinhold Publishing Corporation, New York, 1960.

Sisler, H., VanderWerf, C., and Davidson, A., "College Chemistry—a Systematic Approach," 2nd ed., pp. 123–127, The Macmillan Company, New York, 1961.

_____

chapter three

RELATION OF PROPERTIES
TO BOND TYPE

WE FOUND IN THE preceding chapter that the type of bond
which two atoms will form can be predicted from their electronic structures or their positions in the Periodic Chart. In
this chapter, we seek an answer to the following question:
What reliable predictions can be made concerning the chemical and physical properties of a product which contains a
given type of bond? Answering this question is most important, since much of the work of the modern chemist has to
do with the synthesis of new substances with predetermined
sets of properties. The chemist of today has with some justice
been referred to as a molecular architect, for he designs and
builds new molecules to order. If he is to be successful in
this activity, the chemist must thoroughly understand the relationship between the various "structural elements" in his
molecules and the properties which are desired. Among the
more important of these "structural elements" are the bonds
which hold the atoms of the molecule together.

We shall, therefore, in this chapter classify chemical substances in terms of the kinds of bonds which hold their atoms
together and discuss the various properties which the presence
of these bonds in the structure confer upon the substance.

Realizing at the start that any mode of classification which we adopt will be imperfect and that there will (with any system of classification we adopt) be substances which do not fit perfectly into one class or another but fall somewhere between two or more of the classes, we shall use the following five classes of substances: (a) ionic substances, (b) nonpolar covalent substances, (c) polar covalent substances, (d) network solids, and (e) metals and intermetallic phases.

Ionic Substances

As discussed in the last chapter, ionic substances are formed by the transfer of electrons from atoms of one element to those of another element with the formation of positive and negative ions. The crystal lattices of ionic substances consist of a regular geometrical array of these positive and negative ions, and do not contain any structural unit analogous to the neutral molecule which is the product of covalent bonding between elements. Fig. 3.1a is a drawing illustrating the structure of solid sodium chloride, a typical ionic solid. It will be noted that each Na^+ ion is surrounded by six equidistant Cl^- ions, and further that each Cl^- ion is surrounded by six equidistant Na^+ ions. There is no discrete NaCl unit in the crystal. Other typical ionic crystals are illustrated in Fig. 3.1. Not only are all of these structures different in their geometrical arrangements, but many other types of arrangements of ions are found in ionic crystals. The differences in their geometrical arrangements result from differences in the ratios of positive to negative ions in their formulas and from differences in the relative sizes of the positive and negative ions. However, all these ionic crystals have in common the fact that their structural units are individual ions rather than neutral molecules.

It should be noted that some ionic substances contain ions which consist of more than one atom. Thus, the crystal of calcium carbonate consists of a lattice of Ca^{2+} ions and CO_3^{2-}

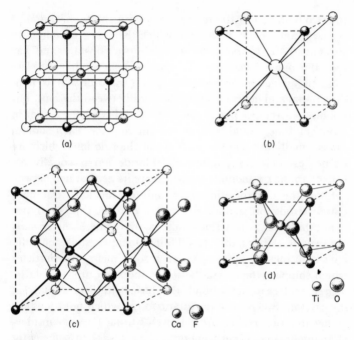

Fig. 3.1. Some typical ionic crystal structures: (a) NaCl, (b) CsCl, (c) CaF₂ (fluorite), (d) TiO₂ (rutile).

ions. The crystal, however, does not contain any $CaCO_3$ molecules.

The forces which hold the particles in ionic crystals together are principally the Coulombic forces of electrostatic attraction between the positive and negative ions. The magnitude of electrostatic attraction between charged bodies is given by the formula

$$F = e_1 e_2 / Dr^2 \quad \text{(Coulomb's Law)}$$

where F is the force of attraction, e_1 and e_2 are the charges on the two bodies, r is the distance between the bodies, and D is a constant for the medium in which the charged bodies are suspended. D is known as the dielectric constant and has the value one in a vacuum. This formula shows that the electrostatic attraction between ions in an ionic crystal is non-directional and depends on the distance between the ions, but not on their relative placement in space. The result is that in a typical ionic crystal such as sodium chloride, each sodium ion is equally attracted to each of the chloride ions which are its nearest neighbors, and each chloride ion is equally attracted to the six sodium ions which are its nearest neighbors.

Since the electrostatic forces between the ions are moderately strong forces, and since in breaking the crystal a number of these ionic attractions must be overcome, ionic crystals are usually rather hard. In addition, ionic crystals generally have high melting points. When a solid melts, the particles which compose the crystal lattice of the solid are, to a large degree, set free from the bonds that have held them in place in the crystal. Since the electrostatic forces which hold ions together in ionic crystals are relatively strong forces, considerable amounts of thermal energy are necessary to sufficiently overcome these forces to allow the crystals to liquefy; thus, melting occurs only at relatively high temperatures.

Furthermore, ionic crystals are not only hard but also quite brittle, that is, they cannot be appreciably deformed without breaking. This brittleness exists because the stability of an ionic crystal depends on the maintenance of the arrangement in which positive ions are surrounded by negative ions and negative ions by positive ions. Take, for example, Fig. 3.2 which represents a cross section through a sodium chloride crystal. Note what happens as any one layer of ions is moved one unit distance relative to an adjacent layer. Between these two layers which have been displaced relative to

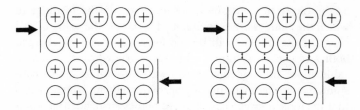

Fig. 3.2. Effect of deformation on an ionic crystal.

each other, the situation across the interface is no longer one in which ions of opposite charge are in contact with each other, but rather one in which all ions of like charge are in contact with each other. Hence, the electrostatic force across this interface is repulsive rather than attractive and the two layers fly apart. Thus, attempts to deform an ionic crystal result in its being broken.

Although ionic crystals are composed of positive and negative ions, ionic substances are not conductors of electricity in the solid state. To conduct an electric current a substance must contain charged bodies which are capable of motion to carry the current. We have seen that in the solid state the ions in ionic substances are fixed in position in the crystal lattice. When, however, the ionic substance is melted and the ions set free in the liquid state, the substance becomes an excellent conductor of electricity. Many important industrial processes depend upon the electrolyses of molten ionic substances, as, for example, the production of metallic sodium by the electrolysis of molten sodium chloride.

Finally, the nature of the forces between the particles in an ionic crystal determine to a large extent the type of solvents in which the substance will be most soluble. We have previously observed that the formula for the force between two charged bodies contains in the denominator a factor known as the dielectric constant which depends on the medium in which the charges are suspended. The larger the value of this constant the smaller will be the force between two charged bodies at a given distance. The dielectric constant D has a value of one in a vacuum, but in water the value of this constant at room temperature is approximately 80, which means that the force between two charged bodies suspended in water at a given distance will be only 1/80th of the force between them at the same distance in a vacuum.

When an ionic crystal goes into solution in a liquid solvent, the forces between the ions must be overcome or greatly reduced. It is not surprising, therefore, to find that ionic substances tend to be more soluble in solvents of high dielectric constant than in solvents of low dielectric constant. Water, for example, with its high dielectric constant, is an excellent solvent for many ionic substances. Carbon tetrachloride with a dielectric constant of only about 2 is an exceedingly poor solvent for ionic substances. There are, of course, other characteristics of solvents which affect their ability to dissolve ionic substances, notably the ability of the solvent molecule to interact or form bonds with one or both of the types of ions in the crystal. However, dielectric constant is one of the most critical factors in determining the solubility of ionic substances in a given solvent.

It should further be noted that when ionic crystals are dissolved in solvents of high dielectric constant, just as when they are melted, the resulting liquid is an excellent conductor of electricity. This is to be expected, for when ionic crystals dissolve in these solvents their ions are free to move under the influence of an electric potential and can carry an electric current.

The vaporization of ionic substances normally does not result in the formation of a gas composed of free ions; rather it normally results in a gas composed of clumps of equal numbers of positive and negative ions. In many instances, as in the case of sodium chloride, ion pairs are formed. When an attempt is made to heat sodium chloride vapor sufficiently to dissociate the ion pairs into free sodium and chloride ions, dissociation into free sodium and chlorine atoms occurs instead. Since the vaporization of an ionic liquid would be opposed by strong, electrostatic interactions between positive and negative ions, ionic substances commonly have very low volatilities and high boiling points.

Nonpolar Covalent Substances

We have already seen (p. 44) that when a pair of electrons is shared between two atoms with equal attractions for these electrons, the resulting bond has no polarity and is known as a nonpolar covalent bond. Molecules containing only such bonds have perfectly symmetrical distributions of positive and negative charge and are, therefore, nonpolar as a whole. Nonpolar substances belonging to this class include hydrogen (H_2), oxygen (O_2), sulfur (S_8), and phosphorus (P_4).

Nonpolar covalent molecules may, however, arise in another manner. In molecules containing a number of identical polar covalent bonds symmetrically distributed in space, the geometry of the molecule is such that the polarities of the various bonds oppose each other in such a way as to give to the molecule a resultant polarity of zero. Examples of such nonpolar molecules are silicon tetrafluoride (SiF_4), carbon dioxide (CO_2), monogermane (GeH_4), and carbon tetrachloride (CCl_4). The spatial configurations of the SiF_4 and CO_2 molecules and the distributions of their bond polarities are illustrated in Fig. 3.3. For completeness of the discussion we should point out that in calculating the resultant polarity of a molecule, it is necessary to consider the polarities which result from the unsymmetrical distribution of unshared electrons in the valence shells of the atoms in the molecule. Some-

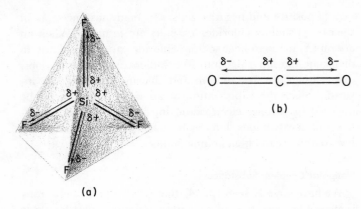

Fig. 3.3. Structures of molecules of silicon tetrafluoride (a) and carbon dioxide (b) showing how bond polarities in asymmetrical molecules cancel to yield a nonpolar molecule.

times contributions to the polarity from these unshared pairs can be quite significant (p. 78).

Crystals consisting of nonpolar covalent molecules are, in general, very weak crystals, since the forces which hold these molecules together in the crystal are only the very weak Van der Waals forces. The arrangement of I_2 molecules in crystalline iodine, a typical nonpolar molecular crystal, is illustrated in Fig. 3.4. The crystals are, therefore, very soft, and have very low melting points. They are nonconductors of electricity, for the crystals contain no charged bodies free to move under the influence of an electrical field.

Again because of the very weak, intermolecular forces which characterize nonpolar covalent substances, the solid and liquid forms of these substances have high volatilities and the liquids have very low boiling points. Since even in the liquid state these substances contain no free charged bodies, the liquids, like the solids, are nonconductors of electricity.

It may readily be shown that the dielectric constant of a

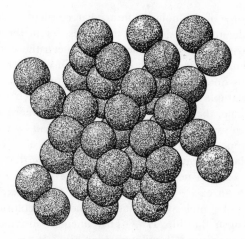

Fig. 3.4. Section of an iodine crystal—a typical non-polar molecular crystal. (From Sisler, VanderWerf, and Davidson, "College Chemistry—a Systematic Approach," 2nd ed., The Macmillan Company, New York, 1961.)

liquid is very closely related to the polarity of the molecules which make up the liquid. Liquids whose molecules are non-polar have very small dielectric constants. Nonpolar molecular liquids are, therefore, generally poor solvents for ionic substances.

Since the weak van der Waals forces between nonpolar molecules are easily broken, such substances are ordinarily present in the gaseous state in the form of single, nonassociated molecules.

Polar Covalent Substances

Polar covalent substances are those which consist of molecules in which there is an unsymmetrical distribution of positive and negative charge, or, in other words, molecules in which the center of positive charge (from the atomic nuclei) and the center of negative charge (from the electrons) do not coincide. Such molecules are called *dipoles*.

The source of the polarity in a polar covalent molecule is easily understood for diatomic molecules, for in these cases, polarity arises simply from the bond between the two atoms being a polar covalent bond, i.e., a bond in which the pair of electrons is unequally shared between the two atoms (p. 44). A good example of such a molecule is hydrogen chloride. In this molecule, the pair of electrons is attracted more strongly by the highly electronegative chlorine atom than by the much less electronegative hydrogen atom. The pair of electrons is thus displaced toward the chlorine atom causing that atom to bear an excess of negative charge and leaving the hydrogen atom with an excess of positive charge. Other examples of diatomic polar molecules include iodine monochloride, ICl, and hydrogen fluoride, HF. This unequal distribution of electronic charge in ICl is illustrated in Fig. 3.5.

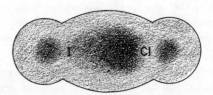

Fig. 3.5. A simple, diatomic, polar molecule—ICl. Note that the electron charge cloud is displaced toward the more electronegative atom—chlorine.

In molecules containing more than two atoms, and hence more than one covalent bond, the situation is more complex. In such instances, the polarity of the molecule is the resultant of the polarities of all the individual bonds in the molecule. We have already seen (p. 73) that molecules containing a number of equivalent polar covalent bonds arranged symmetrically are nonpolar. If, on the other hand, a molecule contains a number of covalent bonds and the bonds are not arranged symmetrically or are not all equivalent or perhaps both, the molecule will have a resultant polarity and will be a dipole. Thus, since we know that because of the difference in electronegativity of hydrogen and oxygen the hydrogen to oxygen bond is polar and since we know that water is a polar molecule, we are sure that the structure of the water molecule is not linear as in Fig. 3.6a, but is angular as in Fig. 3.6b. Likewise, we have seen (p. 73) that because of the

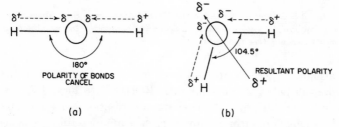

(a)   (b)

Fig. 3.6. Relation of the polarity of the water molecule to its angular configuration. If the molecule were linear as at the left, the bond polarities would cancel and the water molecule would be nonpolar.

symmetrical arrangement of the carbon to chlorine bonds in carbon tetrachloride, the carbon tetrachloride molecule has a zero polarity. In chloroform, $HCCl_3$, there is a similar symmetry of bond arrangement. However, since the polarity of the carbon to hydrogen bond is much less than the polarity of the carbon to chlorine bond, the resultant of the one C—H bond and the three C—Cl bonds is not zero, and the chloroform molecule has a net polarity (Fig. 3.7). Chloroform, therefore, behaves as a polar covalent substance.

In addition to the contributions from the polarities of the individual bonds in the molecule, unshared electron pairs may

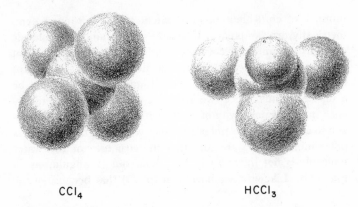

CCl₄   HCCl₃

Fig. 3.7. Structures of the CCl₄ and HCCl₃ molecules. (From Sisler, VanderWerf, and Davidson, "College Chemistry—a Systematic Approach," 2nd ed., The Macmillan Company, New York, 1961.)

also under certain circumstances make a contribution to the over-all polarity of a molecule. Reference to Figs. 1.7, 1.8, and 1.9 will show that the charge distribution corresponding to a pair of electrons in any s, p, or d atomic orbital is symmetrical with respect to the atomic nucleus. The same is true of f orbitals. However, we have seen (p. 38) that in the process of the formation of covalent bonds, the orbitals in the valence shells of the combining atoms are in many instances rearranged or "hybridized" and the new orbitals are individually no longer symmetrical with respect to the atomic nucleus but extend unidirectionally into space.

Unshared electron pairs in such unsymmetrical orbitals contribute to the polarity of the molecule. The nitrogen trifluoride molecule is an example of such a contribution. The nitrogen and fluorine atoms in the nitrogen trifluoride molecule have been shown by structural studies to be arranged in the pyramidal configuration shown in Fig. 3.8. The fact that the over-all polarity of the nitrogen trifluoride molecule is

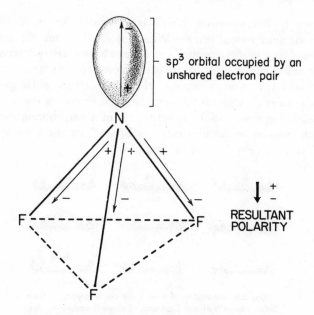

Fig. 3.8. Structure of the NF_3 molecule showing contributions to its polarity from the three N—F bonds and from the unshared electron pair.

much less than the calculated resultant of three N—F bonds arranged in accordance with this structure has been explained as resulting from the fact that the orbital (an sp^3 hybrid) in which the unshared pair of electrons on the nitrogen atoms resides is directed in such a way that the polarity contributed by this electron pair opposes and to a considerable degree cancels the resultant polarity of the three N—F bonds. The result is that the NF_3 molecule has only a moderate polarity. In general, then, the polarity of a molecule is the resultant of the polarities of all the bonds and the polarities of all the unshared electron pairs in the molecule.

The forces between polar molecules are, in general, greater

than the forces between nonpolar molecules, for, in addition to the omnipresent van der Waals forces, there are the additional and sometimes much stronger electrostatic attractions arising from the polar nature of the molecules. Because of the mutual attraction of opposite electrical charges, polar molecules interact with each other, the positive end of one molecule being drawn to the negative end of a neighboring molecule, and so on, as illustrated in Fig. 3.9 for the crystalline state and in Fig. 3.10 for the liquid state.

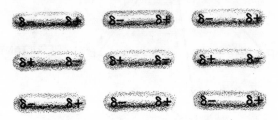

Fig. 3.9. Orientation of polar molecules in crystals. (From Sisler, VanderWerf, and Davidson, "College Chemistry—a Systematic Approach," 2nd ed., The Macmillan Company, New York, 1961.)

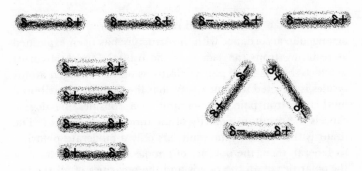

Fig. 3.10. Orientation of polar molecules in liquids. (From Sisler, VanderWerf, and Davidson, "College Chemistry—a Systematic Approach," 2nd ed., The Macmillan Company, New York, 1961.)

Because polar covalent substances have larger intermolecular forces than do nonpolar covalent substances, polar molecular substances in general not only form harder crystals but also have lower volatilities, higher melting points, and higher boiling points than do nonpolar molecular substances. With respect to these properties polar molecular substances are intermediate between nonpolar molecular substances on the one hand and ionic substances on the other. In addition to the examples of polar molecular substances already given, we might list such substances as ethyl alcohol (C_2H_5OH), sulfuric acid (H_2SO_4), nitric acid (HNO_3), phosphoryl chloride ($OPCl_3$), and ammonia (NH_3).

Hydrogen Bonding

In many familiar polar molecular substances there is an intermolecular attractive force in addition to the Van der Waals forces and electrostatic dipole interactions discussed above. It has been found that molecules which contain hydrogen atoms bonded to small, highly electronegative atoms such as nitrogen, oxygen, or fluorine, have a tendency to form a union with other molecules containing electronegative atoms such as these. It has been further established that this union occurs through the hydrogen atom; in other words, the hydrogen atom forms a bridge between the two small, electronegative atoms. These linkages, known appropriately enough as *hydrogen bonds*, are not as strong as ordinary covalent bonds; however, they are quite strong enough to add appreciably to the tendency for molecules in the solid, liquid, and in some instances even in the gaseous state to associate. Moreover, they have sufficient strength to modify considerably the structures of crystals, and they can produce major effects on the physical and chemical properties of substances in which they occur. In any case, they add appreciably to intermolecular forces, usually much more than ordinary polarity of the molecule.

For example, hydrogen bonds account for the extremely un-usual physical properties of water in the solid and liquid states. We know that the freezing point and boiling point of water are considerably higher than would be predicted from corresponding data for the hydrogen compounds of other members of the oxygen family in the periodic chart. This is understandable if we consider that many hydrogen bonds must be broken when ice melts to the liquid state, that many additional hydrogen bonds remain to be broken as liquid water vaporizes, and that the breaking of these bonds requires the additional thermal energy available at the higher temperatures. Also, it can be observed that ice contracts when it melts and the resulting liquid continues to contract as the temperature is raised until a temperature of 3.98° C is reached. This arises because the hydrogen bonds formed between water molecules hold the water molecules in an "open network" structure in the ice crystal. As the ice melts, a considerable proportion of the hydrogen bonds are broken, the ice structure collapses, and the resulting liquid occupies less space than the original solid. Some of the original struc-ture persists in the liquid state and, as the temperature of the liquid is raised, there are two opposing tendencies with respect to volume change: (a) the normal tendency for the liquid to expand as a result of the increase in molecular motion, and (b) the tendency for the liquid to contract as a result of the continued breaking of hydrogen bonds and the resulting collapse of the residual elements of the "ice" struc-ture. The resultant of these two opposing tendencies is that the volume of the sample of water passes through a minimum (the density passes through a maximum) at a temperature of 3.98° C. The hydrogen-bonded structure of ice is illustrated in Fig. 3.11.

Polar Liquids

In addition to the effects produced by the association of polar molecules in the liquid state, the polarity of the mole-

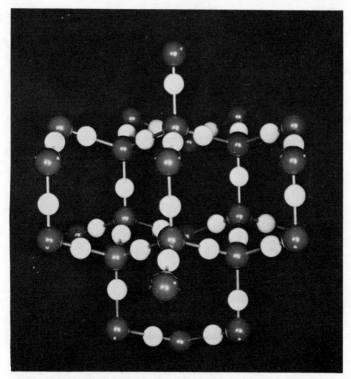

Fig. 3.11. Photograph of a model of a section of an ice crystal. Note the tetrahedral arrangement of the oxygen atoms (dark spheres) connected by hydrogen bonds. Note that each of the hydrogen atoms is nearer one oxygen atom than the other. (From Sisler, VanderWerf, and Davidson, "College Chemistry—a Systematic Approach," 2nd ed., The Macmillan Company, New York, 1961.)

cules has the effect of modifying the properties of the liquid by causing the liquid to have an increased dielectric constant. If the liquid is placed between the plates of a condenser and an electric field applied, the molecules will tend to orient themselves so that the positive ends of the molecules point toward the negative plate of the condenser and the negative ends of the molecules toward the positive plate of the condenser as shown in Fig. 3.12. This orientation has the effect of partially neutralizing the applied electric field, thus reducing the electrostatic attraction between the plates. In other

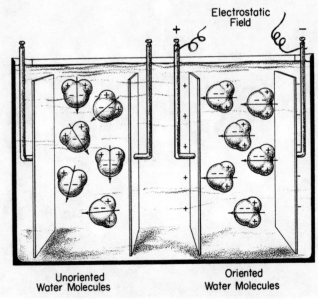

Fig. 3.12. Orientation of polar molecules in an electrostatic field.

words the polarity of the molecules results in the liquid having a higher dielectric constant than would otherwise be the case. In general, highly polar liquids have high dielectric constants. Since the tendency for the molecules of a liquid to orient themselves in an electric field is opposed by the tendency toward randomization resulting from the thermal motion of the molecules, the dielectric constant of a liquid is also a function of temperature—the dielectric constant decreasing with increasing temperature. Because of their high dielectric constants, highly polar liquids tend to be good solvents for ionic solids (p. 72). This effect is commonly enhanced by the strong tendency of polar molecules to be attracted by their negative ends to positive ions, and by their positive ends to negative ions. This formation of solvated ions makes, in a number of instances, a considerable contribution toward overcoming the lattice energy of the ionic crystal and increasing the solubility of an ionic substance in the polar solvent. The solvating effect of water molecules on sodium and chloride ions in the dissolving of sodium chloride in water is illustrated in Fig. 3.13.

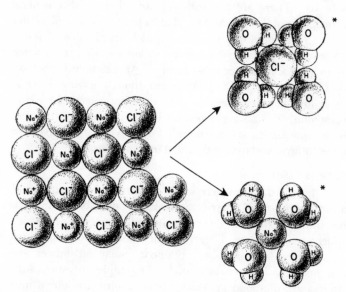

Fig. 3.13. Dissolving of sodium chloride in water showing the hydration of the Na+ and Cl− ions.

*Only four molecules of water are shown but the actual degree of hydration is probably larger than this. (From Sisler, VanderWerf, and Davidson, "College Chemistry—a Systematic Approach," 2nd ed., The Macmillan Company, New York, 1961.)

Polar liquids also tend to be good solvents for other polar molecular substances but poor solvents for nonpolar molecular substances. This effect arises principally from polar molecular solutes being able to enter into dipole-dipole association (p. 80) with the polar solvent molecules. This association helps to overcome the intermolecular forces in the pure solute and promotes solubility. Since, however, nonpolar molecules do not interact in this way with polar solute molecules, the dipole-dipole interactions between the polar solvent molecules tend to "squeeze out" the nonpolar solute molecules, thus reducing their tendency to dissolve in polar solvents. There are a number of exceptions to this general principle; notable is the fact that solvents whose molecules have a relatively low polarity but which are capable of forming hydrogen bonds with certain polar solutes are in some cases good solvents for those solutes. An example is the solvent acetone, $(CH_3)_2C{=}O$, which though having a relatively low dielectric constant is an excellent solvent for many compounds containing hydrogen linked to nitrogen, oxygen, or fluorine atoms; acetone readily forms hydrogen bonds with these solutes, and thus takes them into solution.

Network Solids

In those instances where solids are formed by the union of atoms by means of polar or nonpolar covalent bonds into an indefinitely extended three-dimensional network, properties which are distinctly different from those of polar or nonpolar molecular solids are obtained. Such substances are commonly called network solids. Examples of such substances are diamond in which carbon atoms are joined into an indefinitely extended network in which each carbon atom is attached by nonpolar covalent bonds to four other carbon atoms (Fig. 3.14), silicon carbide which has a similar structure in which each silicon atom is surrounded by four carbon atoms and each carbon atom by four silicon atoms,

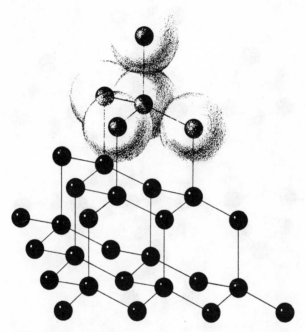

Fig. 3.14. Structure of diamond. (From Sisler, VanderWerf, and Davidson, "College Chemistry—a Systematic Approach," 2nd ed., The Macmillan Company, New York, 1961.)

and quartz, SiO_2 (Fig. 3.15), in which each silicon atom is connected to four oxygen atoms and each oxygen atom to two silicon atoms by polar covalent bonds. In network solids the entire crystal may be thought of as a single molecule. Since the breaking, melting, or vaporization of such a crystal requires the breaking of a multitude of quite stable covalent bonds, it is not surprising that network solids are exceedingly hard and have, in general, very high melting points. Morever, since the solution of substances of this type in liquid solvents also requires the breaking of a large proportion of the

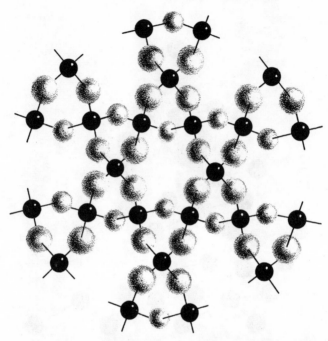

Fig. 3.15. Structure of quartz. Black circles represent silicon atoms. Oxygen atoms lie at different heights relative to the plane of the paper. (From Sisler, VanderWerf, and Davidson, "College Chemistry—a Systematic Approach," 2nd ed., The Macmillan Company, New York, 1961.)

covalent bonds in the crystal, it is to be expected that network solids will be virtually insoluble in ordinary liquid solvents of either the polar or nonpolar type. As a matter of fact, the only substances which dissolve network solids are those which react chemically with them.

Solids which are intermediate in structure between molecular crystals on the one hand and three-dimensional network solids such as those discussed above on the other, include solids which have layer-type lattices, containing aggregates of atoms bound by covalent bonds and indefinitely extended in *two* dimensions and solids which have chain-type lattices containing aggregates of atoms bound by covalent bonds and indefinitely extended in *one* dimension. Examples of layer-type lattices include graphite which, as is indicated in Fig. 3.16, contains indefinitely extended layers of carbon atoms made up of fused hexagonal rings, and the hexagonal form of boron nitride which is also made up of layers consisting of

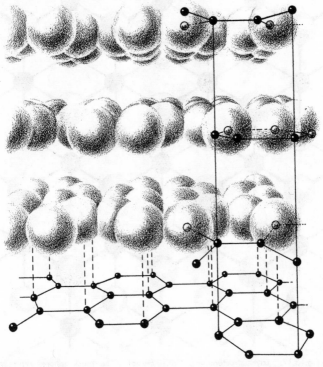

Fig. 3.16. Structure of graphite. (From Sisler, VanderWerf, and Davidson, "College Chemistry—a Systematic Approach," 2nd ed., The Macmillan Company, New York, 1961.)

fused hexagonal rings in which boron and nitrogen atoms appear alternately. Many substances usually supposed to be ionic or polar molecular solids have layer-type or, in a few instances, chain-type lattices. Anhydrous cadmium chloride is an example, since it has the layer-type structure shown in Fig. 3.17. The bonds within the cadmium chloride layers are

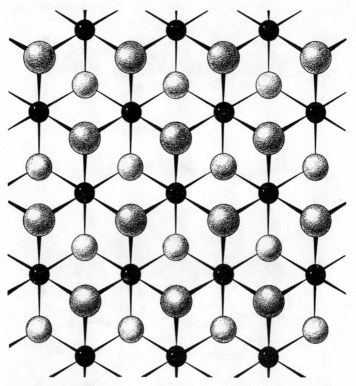

Fig. 3.17. Layer structure in a $CdCl_2$ crystal. The black spheres represent cadmium atoms in the plane of the paper, the larger gray spheres chlorine atoms in front of this plane, the smaller gray spheres chlorine atoms behind this plane. Note that each cadmium atom is surrounded octahedrally by six chlorine atoms.

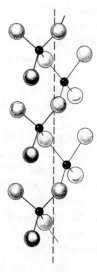

Fig. 3.18a. Structure of an $(SO_3)_x$ chain in crystalline sulfur trioxide. The black spheres represent sulfur atoms.

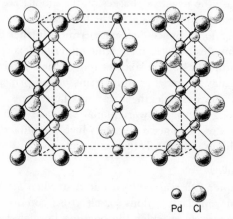

Pd Cl

Fig. 3.18b. Structure of crystalline $PdCl_2$. Note the $(PdCl_2)_x$ chains.

polar covalent.   Examples of solids containing chain-type structures include one form of sulfur trioxide (Fig. 3.18a), as well as beryllium chloride and palladium chloride (Fig. 3.18b). Substances with these layer-type and chain-type lattices lack the hardness and highly refractory character of three-dimensional solids.   In a very rough way their properties may be said to be intermediate between polar molecular crystals and network solids.

It should also be noted that there are crystalline solids which may be considered to have types of structures which are intermediate between those of ionic solids and network solids. This group includes the many mineral silicates which contain indefinitely extended or polymeric anions.   In some instances, the silicate anion is indefinitely extended in one dimension to give a chain-type anion (Fig. 3.19a); in other cases the silicate anion is indefinitely extended in two dimensions to give a layer-type anion (Fig. 3.19b).   Some of the aluminosilicate minerals contain anions which are indefinitely extended in three dimensions to give a three-dimensional network anion. In each case the negative charges on the anions are balanced by the presence in the crystal of the necessary number of simple metal cations. Space does not permit a further discussion of these complex but very interesting materials, except to state that the properties of the silicates reflect their internal structures and may be understood in terms of the principles here presented. For example, the micas have layer-type anions and have a strong tendency toward planar cleavage. On the other hand, asbestos, a mineral silicate which contains chain-type anions exhibits a markedly fibrous structure.

Metallic Solids

In Chapter 2 it was pointed out that when atoms having similar but small attractions for electrons combine, metallic phases are formed in which the bonding is related to, but is

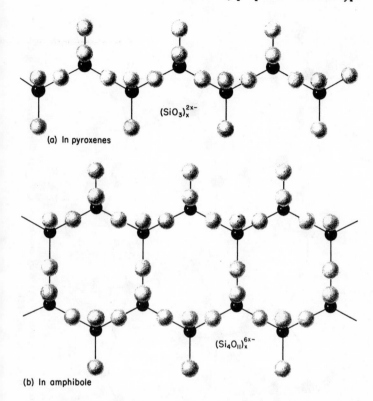

(a) In pyroxenes

$(SiO_3)_x^{2x-}$

(b) In amphibole

$(Si_4O_{11})_x^{6x-}$

Fig. 3.19a. Chain-type silicate anions. (From Sisler, VanderWerf, and Davidson, "College Chemistry—a Systematic Approach," 2nd ed., The Macmillan Company, New York, 1961.)

somewhat different from, covalent bonding. The simplest examples of metallic phases are the pure metals themselves.

The structures of metallic crystals are notable for the fact that the metal atoms are very closely packed in the crystal lattice. There are three principal metal structures, illustrated in Fig. 3.20. They are face-centered cubic close packed (a, b),

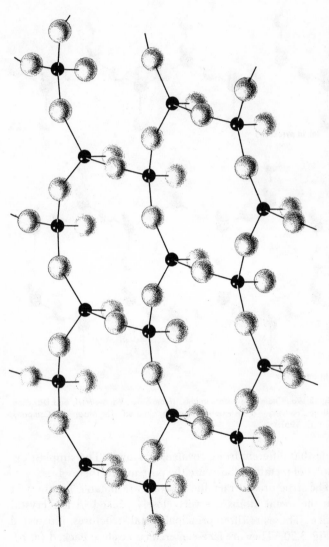

Fig. 3.19b. A layer-type silicate anion. (From Sisler, VanderWerf, and Davidson, "College Chemistry—a Systematic Approach," 2nd ed., The Macmillan Company, New York, 1961.)

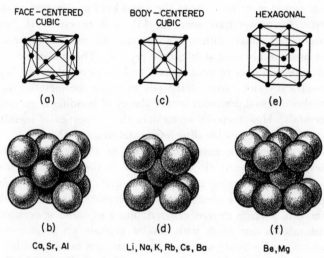

FACE-CENTERED CUBIC

BODY-CENTERED CUBIC

HEXAGONAL

(a)

(c)

(e)

(b)

(d)

(f)

Ca, Sr, Al

Li, Na, K, Rb, Cs, Ba

Be, Mg

Fig. 3.20. Face-centered cubic close packed, body-centered cubic, and hexagonal close packed structures.

body-centered cubic (c, d), and hexagonal close packed (e, f). In the first and third of these, the coordination number of each metal atom is twelve which is the maximum coordination number for the packing of like spheres and thus represents the closest packing possible. In the second type of structure, the coordination number of each metal atom is eight, so the structure is not quite close packed; but it is almost so, for in addition to the eight nearest neighbors which each atom has, there are an additional six atoms only slightly further away.

It is apparent that with coordination numbers of either eight or twelve, and with only a considerably smaller number of valence electrons available per atom (usually one, two, or three for nontransitional metals), each atom in a metal crystal cannot be bound to each of its nearest neighbors by a covalent bond of the ordinary type. Certainly, also, we would not expect ionic bonding of the usual kind in a system of this type, for as we have seen (p. 43), it is necessary to have atoms of strongly differing attractions for valence electrons, in order to obtain a stable ionic crystal. The malleable and ductile character of most metals and, in particular, the high electrical conductivity which characterizes the metallic state makes unusual demands on the theory of bonding in metallic crystals. How then do we explain the properties of metallic crystals in terms of bonding forces and structures?

First it must be noted that atoms of all the metals have several unoccupied electron orbitals in their outer electron shells. Secondly, we may presume that, in the very close-packed structures which are characteristic of metal crystals, there is a large degree of overlapping of these unoccupied orbitals on one atom with similar orbitals on neighboring atoms, and orbitals on these atoms in turn overlap with orbitals on their neighboring atoms, and so on throughout the crystal. Thus it is possible for an electron to move from an orbital in the valence shell of one atom into a similar orbital on another atom with relative ease, and the valence electrons may be considered to be delocalized, i.e., they no longer belong to individual atoms but to the crystal as a whole. As a matter of fact, the wave functions which described the individual orbitals on the isolated atoms are modified and converted into wave functions which describe electronic bands which belong to the whole metal crystal and not to individual atoms. Because of the fact that in the atoms of the metals there is in general a considerable excess of available orbitals over valence electrons, one or more of the electron bands which result from the merging of these orbitals are only partially filled with electrons. Electrons in these partially filled bands have a high degree of mobility, and it is these bands which account for the high electrical conductivity of metallic crystals.

It should be kept in mind, however, that it is only the outermost orbitals and electrons which enter into the type of interaction described above and that the electrons in the inner shells of the various metal atoms remain localized in their individual atomic orbitals. As a very rough first approximation, we may think of a metal crystal as a geometrical array of positive metal ions suspended as it were in a sea of delocalized electrons; it is the existence of electrons in these delocalization bands which results in the bonding force which holds the metal crystal together.

Not only the electrical conductivity but also other properties characteristic of the metallic state may be explained in terms of the above theory of metallic bonding. Since the charge distribution resulting from the bonding electrons is more or less uniform throughout the crystal, the positive ions in the crystal may be moved past one another with relative ease provided that this may be accomplished without appreciably changing the average internuclear distance. As is shown in Fig. 3.21, one group of ions can be changed in position relative to neighboring groups of ions, without changing the type of internal environment of each positive ion; this makes it possible to change the shape of the crystal without breaking it. Thus, the nondirectional bonding which is characteristic of the metallic state is in striking contrast to the directed covalent bonding in network solids. The effects of distorting a metallic crystal are also in strong contrast to the

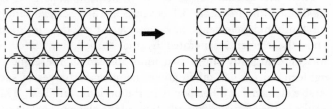

Fig. 3.21. Effect of displacement of atoms in a metal crystal.

situation which arises when ionic crystals are distorted (see p. 71). Thus, of all the crystalline solids, metallic crystals alone have a high degree of malleability and ductility.

The high elasticity characteristic of the metallic state may also be explained in terms of this picture (Fig. 3.21). The fact that ions in the metal crystal may be moved without breaking the crystal means that under stress, some of the ions may be moved out of position slightly, thus allowing the crystal to be temporarily bent; but when the stress is removed, the ions will spring back into their original positions and the crystal will assume its original shape. If, however, the distortion is too great, the ions are permanently moved to a new location, and the crystal is bent permanently into a new shape.

The close packing of atoms in metallic crystals explains the generally high densities of metals. Exceptions occur, of course, in those instances (the alkali metals, for example) where the atoms themselves have rather large radii and where the weights of the individual atoms are rather low (lithium, beryllium, magnesium, and aluminum, for example).

Most metals have moderately high melting points and their crystals are relatively strong. These properties are related to the actual number of bonding electrons per atom as well as the other atomic parameters such as atomic radius and nuclear charge. The following data (Table 3.1) on the melting points of the metals in four successive families of the Periodic Chart illustrate this point.

There are discontinuities between elements separated by the dashed line in Table 3.1 because in each vertical family the lanthanide elements have intervened at this location. Thus the elements separated by the dashed line differ in nuclear charge by thirty two units instead of the eight or eighteen units which differentiate the nuclear charges of successive elements at other points in the periodic families. This results in the electronic distributions of the elements below the

TABLE 3.1. Melting Points of Metals in Four Successive Families of the Periodic Chart

No. of Bonding Electrons per Atom	1	2	3	4
Melting Points °C	K, 64	Ca, 851	Sc, 1397	Ti, 1727
	Rb, 39	Sr, 771	Y, 1477	Zr, 1860
	Cs, 29	Ba, 717	La, 887	Hf, 2327
		Ra, 960	Ac, 1050	Th, 1827

dashed line being somewhat more compact than would otherwise be the case; these elements have lower atomic radii, higher densities, and higher melting points than would be predicted by extrapolation from the lighter members of the respective families (see also p. 56). This effect is sometimes called the *lanthanide contraction*. It affects not only the physical properties of the free metals but also their chemical properties and the properties of their respective compounds.

The high degree of mobility of the valence electrons in metallic crystals helps to explain the rapid transmission of heat through metal crystals, i.e. the fact that metals generally have very high thermal conductivities. Electrons in regions of the metal where the temperature is high can acquire kinetic energy and rapidly transport it through the metal to atoms in cooler parts of the metal. Where electrons are highly localized, as e.g. in network or ionic solids, thermal conductance occurs through transfer of energy from one atom to the atom in its immediate coordination sphere—a much slower process than conduction through the agency of mobile, delocalized electrons.

Finally it should be noted that the successive energy states in the electron bands in metal crystals lie very close together; therefore, metals can absorb light corresponding to a wide range of wavelengths and can re-emit these radiations. Con-

TABLE 3.2 Summary of Characteristics of Principal Types of Crystalline Solids

	Ionic Substances	Polar Molecular Substances
Particles in Crystal	Positive and negative ions	Polar molecules
Attractive Forces between Particles	Electrostatic attractions between ions (strong) plus van der Waals forces (weak)	Electrostatic attractions between molecular dipoles (variable strength) plus van der Waals forces (weak). In some cases hydrogen bonds in addition
Melting Points and Boiling Points	High	Intermediate
Electrical Conductance of Solid	Very low	Very low
Electrical Conductance of Liquid	High	Very low
Other Physical Characteristics of the Solid	Hard; brittle; more soluble in polar than in nonpolar liquids	Much weaker than ionic crystals. More soluble in polar than nonpolar liquids.
Conditions for Formation	Formed between atoms which have markedly different attractions for outer shell electrons; i.e. between active metals and active nonmetals	Formed from molecules containing polar bonds unsymmetrically distributed in the molecule. Such bonds are formed between atoms having a moderate difference in attraction for outer shell electrons but with both attractions being high
Examples	NaCl, KBr, MgF$_2$, BaO, CuSO$_4$, CsNO$_3$	H$_2$O, ICl, NF$_3$, C$_6$H$_5$COOH, CH$_3$NH$_2$
A Typical Structure		

Radius of Chloride⁻ Ion   Radius of Sodium⁺ Ion

NaCl

O$_2$N —⟨ ⟩— NH$_2$

*H atoms omitted for clarity.

100

TABLE 3.2 (continued)

Nonpolar Molecular Substances	Network Solids	Metallic Substances
Nonpolar molecules	Atoms united by a network of covalent bonds	Positive ions and delocalized electrons
Van der Waals forces (weak)	Covalent bonds (polar or nonpolar) (strong) in which all the electrons are localized	Metallic bonds involving bands of delocalized valence electrons may be considered a special type of covalent bonding
Low	Very high	Mostly high
Very low	Very low	Very high
Extremely low		Very high
Soft, weak crystals; more soluble in nonpolar liquids than in polar liquids	Exceedingly hard. Insoluble in most ordinary liquids	Malleable and ductile; high thermal conductivity; insoluble in all solvents except other metals or those with which metals react
Formed from symmetrical molecules or molecules containing only nonpolar bonds. Such bonds are formed between like atoms or atoms having almost no difference in attraction for outer shell electrons but with both attractions high	Result when the covalences of the elements are such as to form indefinitely extended networks instead of finite molecules.	Formed between atoms of similar attraction for outer-shell electrons but with both attractions low
H_2, Cl_2, CO_2, SiH_4, CCl_4, I_2	Diamond, SiC, AlN, SiO_2, BN ("borazon")	All metals and alloys

CO_2 SiC   Mg

sequently, metals are characterized by opaqueness (all very finely divided metals are black in color), high reflectivity, and a lustrous appearance.

Summary

In this chapter we have examined the properties of five principal types of crystalline solids and the liquids which they form when melted, and have interpreted these properties in terms of the bonding forces and structures which are characteristic of these substances. The chief points in the discussion are summarized in Table 3.2.

Suggested Readings

Coulson, C. A., "Valence," 2nd ed., pp. 303–343, Oxford University Press, London, 1961.

Emeléus, H., and Anderson, J., "Modern Aspects of Inorganic Chemistry," 3rd ed., pp. 482–516, Routledge and Kegan Paul Ltd., London, 1960.

Kleinberg, J., Argersinger, W., and Griswold, E., "Inorganic Chemistry," pp. 147–207, D. C. Heath and Company, Boston, 1960.

Sisler, H., VanderWerf, C., and Davidson, A., "College Chemistry —a Systematic Approach," 2nd ed., pp. 137–151, 506–525, The Macmillan Company, New York, 1961.

Sisler, H., VanderWerf, C., and Davidson, A., "General Chemistry —a Systematic Approach," 2nd ed., pp. 178–196, The Macmillan Company, New York, 1959.

chapter four ——————————————————

SOME EXAMPLES OF
CHEMICAL AND
PHYSICAL PERIODICITY

IN THE LIMITED amount of space still remaining in this small book, we shall consider a few groups of compounds which illustrate the correlation of properties with structure and position in the periodic system. These series include the binary hydrogen compounds, the binary oxygen compounds, and the binary halides. Finally, we shall consider briefly the most recently discovered and currently most interesting new family of compounds, viz. the compounds of elements of the helium family commonly known as Group 0 and up until recently classified as the "inert gases."

The Binary Hydrogen Compounds

Some of the simpler binary hydrides of the nontransitional elements are listed in Table 4.1 in the order of the location of the respective elements in the Periodic Chart. It will be interesting to observe the changes in physical and chemical properties of the hydrogen compounds which occur as we pass from compound to compound along a given horizontal row. Consider, for example, the sequence of compounds

$$LiH, \ BeH_2, \ B_2H_6, \ CH_4, \ NH_3, \ H_2O, \ HF$$

TABLE 4.1. Some Simple Binary Hydrides of the Nontransitional Elements

Decreasing hydridic character—increasing protonic character →

LiH	BeH$_2$			B$_2$H$_6$	CH$_4$	NH$_3$	H$_2$O	HF
NaH	MgH$_2$	—		(AlH$_3$)$_x$	SiH$_4$	PH$_3$	H$_2$S	HCl
KH	CaH$_2$	—	ZnH$_2$	Ga$_2$H$_6$	GeH$_4$	AsH$_3$	H$_2$Se	HBr
RbH	SrH$_2$	—	CdH$_2$	InH$_3$	SnH$_4$	SbH$_3$	H$_2$Te	HI
CsH	BaH$_2$	—	HgH$_2$	TlH$_3$	PbH$_4$	BiH$_3$	H$_2$Po	HAt
Ionic (Saline) Hydrides		Intermediate		Covalent Hydrides				

Increasing hydridic character ↓ (left margin)

Change from ionic to covalent bonding →

Change from basic character to acidic character →

Hydrogen itself is intermediate in its attraction for electrons as exemplified by an electronegativity value of 2.1 on the Pauling scale; whereas the elements with which the hydrogen is combined in this series have values (Table 2.7) which change progressively from 1.0 to 4.0 as follows:

Li, 1.0; Be, 1.5; B, 2.0; C, 2.5; N, 3.0; O, 3.5; F, 4.0

Thus, in the above sequence of compounds, the polarity of the M—H bond changes direction. In lithium hydride the charge on the hydrogen atom is negative, whereas in the highly polar hydrogen fluoride molecule, the hydrogen atom forms the positive end of the dipole. The physical and chemical properties of the compounds reflect this change in polarity.

Lithium hydride is essentially an ionic compound, the crystal containing Li$^+$ and H$^-$ ions. When the molten compound is electrolyzed, hydrogen gas is discharged at the anode. Because of the very strong tendency for the H$^-$ ion to accept protons from such proton donors as water, alcohols, and ammonia

$$H:^- + H:A \longrightarrow H:H + :A^-$$

lithium hydride is an exceedingly strong base.

As would be expected from the somewhat higher electronegativity of beryllium than of lithium, and the correspondingly lesser difference in electronegativity of beryllium and hydrogen than of lithium and hydrogen, beryllium hydride is considerably less ionic than is lithium hydride. Nevertheless the hydrogen in beryllium hydride is considerably negative, i.e., has a considerable degree of *hydridic* character. Like lithium hydride, beryllium hydride reacts with active proton donors with great vigor, to release gaseous hydrogen. Because of the tendency for hydride ions to form a bridge between two small multiply-charged positive ions, beryllium hydride crystals are probably composed of polymeric species of the following type:

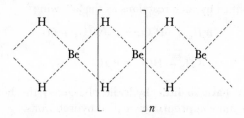

Boron and hydrogen have almost the same electronegativity. The hydrogen atoms in boron hydrides are, therefore, only slightly negative in character. Since the boron atom has three valence electrons, it might be expected that boron would form a compound with the formula BH_3. However, there is in this species an unused orbital in the valence shell of the boron atom, and two BH_3 units combine to form the compound B_2H_6 in which the two boron atoms are bonded together by two hydride bridges as illustrated below.

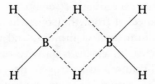

These hydride bridges involve the use of one pair of electrons to tie three atoms together and are examples of what is sometimes called *three-center bonds*. Boron forms a variety of hydrides, all of which contain one or more three-center bonds. The more important of these, in addition to B_2H_6, are B_4H_{10}, B_5H_9, B_5H_{11}, B_6H_{10}, and $B_{10}H_{14}$. Although much less hydridic in character than lithium hydride and beryllium hydride, the boron hydrides do exhibit a little hydridic character as exemplified by such reactions as the following:

$$B_2H_6 + 6H_2O \rightarrow 2B(OH)_3 + 6H_2$$

$$B_2H_6 + HCl \rightarrow B_2H_5Cl + H_2$$

Since they have so little hydridic character, the boron hydrides are more appropriately called hydroborons.

As we pass on to the hydrogen compounds of carbon (generally called hydrocarbons), we find that carbon has a slightly higher electronegativity than hydrogen and the carbon-hydrogen bond has a very low polarity in which hydrogen is slightly positive. The large group of hydrocarbons are therefore generally compounds having little polarity. Methane, CH_4, has, of course, no polarity at all since it has a tetrahedral structure in which even the small polarities of the four C—H bonds cancel giving a resultant polarity of zero.

The effect of the low polarity of methane and the other saturated hydrocarbons combined with the lack of any empty orbitals or unshared electron pairs in the valence shells of the carbon atoms causes the saturated hydrocarbons to be relatively unreactive except at elevated temperatures.

Nitrogen differs sufficiently in electronegativity from hydrogen to give to the N—H bond a moderate amount of polarity with the hydrogen atom bearing the positive charge. However, the polarity of the N—H bond is still relatively low and the tendency for the ammonia molecule, NH_3, to release protons is relatively small. Hence, ammonia is only an exceedingly weak acid. In fact, because of the unshared pair of electrons on the nitrogen atom, ammonia has a strong tendency to accept protons, and behaves as a strong base.

Oxygen, with its further increase in electronegativity over that of nitrogen, forms bonds with hydrogen in which the hydrogen atoms are distinctly positive. The polarity of the O—H bonds and the angular configuration of the water molecule (see p. 77) results in the strongly polar character of the water molecule. Water has a considerable tendency to release protons and thus behaves as an acid. Since it can also accept protons by the use of the unshared electron pairs on the oxygen atom, it also behaves as a base. Its basic character is less than that of ammonia and its acidic character is greater than that of ammonia.

Fluorine is the most electronegative of all the elements and the hydrogen fluoride molecule has a large degree of polarity with the hydrogen atom bearing a considerable positive charge. Hydrogen fluoride is, therefore, predominantly acidic in behavior.

Space does not permit a detailed discussion of all the hydrogen compounds but, in general, the trends in all the horizontal rows in Table 4.1 are analogous to those discussed above. Within the elements of a given family (vertical columns in Table 4.1) the trend is toward increasing hydridic character (increasing negative charge on the hydrogen) or decreasing protonic character (decreasing positive charge on the hydrogen) from top to bottom of the family. The apparently anomalous fact that protonic character *decreases* in the sequences $HF > HCl > HBr > HI$; $H_2O > H_2Se > H_2Te$ and $NH_3 > PH_3 > AsH_3 > SbH_3$, whereas acidity in water and similar solvents *increases* in the same sequences, is treated in detail by Professor C. A. VanderWerf in another volume in this series* and will not be discussed further here.

The Binary Compounds of Oxygen

The properties of the oxides of the various elements provide an excellent example of the periodicity of chemical and physical characteristics. Since many of the elements form more than one oxide, we shall, in the following comparisons, consider the oxides in which the respective elements exhibit the maximum oxidation numbers characteristic of the periodic families to which the various elements belong.

Consider, for example, the elements of the third period of the periodic system, viz., Na, Mg, Al, Si, P, S, Cl, and Ar. The oxides corresponding to the maximum oxidation numbers of these elements are as follows:

$$Na_2O, MgO, Al_2O_3, SiO_2, P_4O_{10}, SO_3, Cl_2O_7$$

Oxygen has an electronegativity value of 3.5 in the Pauling scale, and the differences in electronegativities for the elements in each of the compounds in the above series are as follows:

Na_2O	MgO	Al_2O_3	SiO_2	P_4O_{10}	SO_3	Cl_2O_7
2.6	2.3	2.0	1.7	1.4	1.0	0.5

*VanderWerf, C. A., "Acids, Bases, and the Chemistry of the Covalent Bond," p. 50, Reinhold Publishing Corporation, New York, 1961.

In view of these data, it is not surprising that in the above series of oxides the bonding changes from definitely ionic on the left to definitely covalent on the right.

This trend from ionic to covalent character in the bonding in this series of oxides is reflected in the physical properties of the oxides. For example, consider the following melting point data for these oxides:

	Na_2O	MgO	Al_2O_3	SiO_2	P_4O_{10}	SO_3	Cl_2O_7
m.p. (°C)	920	3802	2027	1700	360 (sub-limes)	17 (α-form)	−81.5

Thus, sodium monoxide and magnesium oxide are both ionic, crystalline solids, and have relatively high melting points as is characteristic of such crystals. The melting point of magnesium oxide is much higher than that of sodium oxide because of the much higher lattice energy of the former resulting from the fact that magnesium ion is doubly charged. Aluminum oxide is principally ionic, but there is a slight change in the direction of polar covalency. The silicon to oxygen bond is a covalent bond with a considerable degree of polarity. The melting point of silicon dioxide is, however, high because the SiO_2 crystal is an example of a network solid and the melting of such solids requires the breaking of many of the chemical bonds in the structure. The last three oxides in the series, P_4O_{10}, SO_3, and Cl_2O_7 all form molecular crystals. The P—O and S—O bonds have appreciable polarity. However, the molecules P_4O_{10} and SO_3 are symmetrical and the polarities of the bonds cancel so that the molecules are nonpolar. The Cl_2O_7 molecule has little polarity since the Cl—O bond is itself only slightly polar.

The chemical properties of the oxides of the series likewise reflect the changes in bond type. For example, the acidity or basicity of oxides (and their corresponding hydroxides) can be correlated with the electronegativities of the atom to

which the oxygen atom is bonded.* Thus, the trend in acidity and basicity in the above series of oxides is as follows:

Na_2O	MgO	Al_2O_3	SiO_2	P_4O_{10}	SO_3	Cl_2O_7
strongly basic	basic	amphoteric	weakly acidic	moderately acidic	strongly acidic	very strongly acidic

Decreasing basicity—increasing acidity
$\longrightarrow$

The trends in chemical and physical properties of the oxides
of nontransition elements of other periods in the periodic system are similar to those discussed above. Relationships between the properties of the oxides of the transition elements
are somewhat more complex, although the same general principles apply. Since within any given periodic family electronegativity tends to decrease from top to bottom of the
family, the oxides of the elements of a family tend to become
more ionic (or less covalent) from the top of the family to the
bottom.

Binary Chlorides and Fluorides

The physical properties of the binary halides vary sys-
tematically with position of the elements in the periodic
system in accordance with the nature of the chemical bonds
which characterize the particular compound. Thus, as the
ionic character of the bonds decreases (and covalent character increases) there is a trend toward lower melting point
and less negative equivalent heat of formation. These trends
are illustrated by the data in Table 4.2 for some of the
fluorides of nontransition elements and in Table 4.3 for some
of the chlorides of nontransition elements. These correlations
are not perfect, however, since factors other than bond type

*VanderWerf, C. A., "Acids, Bases, and the Chemistry of the Covalent
Bond," pp. 45, 46, Reinhold Publishing Corporation, New York, 1961.

TABLE 4.2. Melting Points and Equivalent Heats of Formation of Some Fluorides of Nontransition Elements

LiF	BeF_2	BF_3	CF_4	NF_3	OF_1		
845	800	−128.7	−183.7	−208.5	−223.90		(° C.)
−146.3	—	−88.5	−40.6	−9.1	2.25		(kcal./g. equiv.)
NaF	MgF_2	AlF_3	SiF_4	PF_3	(S_2F_2)	ClF	
995	1263	1290	−90.3	−151.5	−120.5	−155.6	(° C.)
−136.0	−131.8	−104	−92.5	—	—	−25.7	(kcal./g. equiv.)
KF	CaF_2·····GaF_3		GeF_4	AsF_3	(SeF_4)	BrF	
856	1418	950	−15.0	−5.95	−80	−33	(° C.)
−134.5	−145.2	—	—	−72.8	—	−18.4	(kcal./g. equiv.)
RbF	SrF_2······InF_3		SnF_4	SbF_3	(TeF_4)	(IF_5)	
775	1400	1170	(sublimes)	290	129.6	8.5	(° C.)
−131.3	−145.2	—	—	−72.4	—	−40.9	(kcal./g. equiv.)
CsF	BaF_2·····TlF_3		PbF_4	BiF_3			
682	1302	550	—	727			(° C.)
−126.9	−143.5	—	—	—			(kcal./g. equiv.)

Decreasing ionic character—increasing covalent character

⟶

Decreasing melting point—heats of formation become less negative

affect melting point and other properties. These other factors include van der Waals forces (which are roughly proportional to molecular weight) and molecular symmetry. Electrical conductances of the halides in the liquid state also tend to decrease from left to right in the periodic chart as do also their boiling points. Since the properties of compounds depend on other aspects of their structure (such as symmetry, for example) as well as bond type, the trends are not always smooth and there are, in fact, some large variations. However, the over-all tendencies are clearly evident.

TABLE 4.3.   Melting Points and Equivalent Heats of Formation of Chlorides of Nontransition Elements

LiCl	BeCl$_2$	BCl$_3$	CCl$_4$	NCl$_3$	OCl$_2$	ClF	
610	440	−107	−22.9	(b.p. < 71)	−116	−155.6	(° C.)
−97.7	−61.2	−33.3$_{(1)}$	−8.3	—	—	−13.3	(kcal./g. equiv.)
NaCl	MgCl$_2$	AlCl$_3$	SiCl$_4$	PCl$_3$	SCl$_2$		
808	714	192	−68	−92	−78		(° C.)
−98.2	−76.7	−55.4	−38.3	−27.0$_{(1)}$	−6.0		(kcal./g. equiv.)
KCl	CaCl$_2$....GaCl$_3$		GeCl$_4$	AsCl$_3$	(Se$_2$Cl$_2$)	BrCl	
772	782	77.5	−49.5	−16	−85	—	(° C.)
−104.2	−95.0	−41.8	−32.5	−26.7	−10.0	3.51$_{(g)}$	(kcal./g. equiv.)
RbCl	SrCl$_2$.....InCl$_3$		SnCl$_4$	SbCl$_3$	TeCl$_2$	ICl	
717	875	(sublimes)	−33.3	73.2	175	27.3	(° C.)
−102.9	−99.0	42.8	−32.6	−30.4	—	4.2$_{(g)}$	(kcal./g. equiv.)
CsCl	BaCl$_2$....TlCl$_3$		PbCl$_4$	BiCl$_3$			
645	962	25	−15	232			(° C.)
−103.5	−102.8	−28.0	—	−30.2			(kcal./g. equiv.)

Decreasing ionic character—increasing covalent character

→

Decreasing melting point—heats of formation become less negative

The properties of the bromides and iodides show trends similar to those exhibited by the fluorides and chlorides except that, in general, ionic character for the halides of a given element decreases in the order fluoride > chloride > bromide > iodide. This is to be expected in view of the following trend in electronegativity: F > Cl > Br > I.

Compounds of the Elements of the Helium Family

Until early in 1962 it was generally believed that the electronic configurations of atoms of the elements helium, neon,

argon, krypton, xenon, and radon are so "stable" that these
elements form only exceedingly weak bonds with other atoms.
Ionic and covalent bonds of the usual types were virtually unknown in the chemistries of these elements and these elements
were, therefore, quite properly called the "inert gases."

Early in 1962 Professor Neil Bartlett of the University of
British Columbia observed that oxygen reacts with platinum
hexafluoride to yield dioxygenyl hexafluoroplatinate(V) in
accordance with the following equation:

$$O_2 + PtF_6 \rightarrow [O_2^+][PtF_6^-]$$

Noting that the ionization energy of xenon (12.12 e.v.) is
virtually the same as that of molecular oxygen (12.2 e.v.),
Professor Bartlett carried out the reaction of xenon with
platinum hexafluoride and obtained the compound $XePtF_6$.
This compound is an orange-yellow solid, insoluble in carbon
tetrachloride, which undergoes rapid hydrolysis in the presence of water vapor:

$$2XePtF_6 + 6H_2O \rightarrow 2Xe + O_2 + 2PtO_2 + 12HF$$

A similar reaction with rhodium hexafluoride was shown to
yield $XeRhF_6$.

Stimulated by this startling development, workers in a
number of laboratories throughout the world began an in-
tensive investigation of the reactions of xenon and other
members of the helium family. As a result, the formation of
a number of new compounds was quickly discovered.

Xenon was shown to react with a stoichiometric excess of
fluorine at 400° C. to yield colorless crystals of a substance
having the molecular formula XeF_4. The same substance can
also be prepared by allowing the mixture of xenon and
fluorine to flow through a hot, nickel tube at dull red heat, and
also by action of an electric discharge on a mixture of xenon
and fluorine at −78° C. Xenon tetrafluoride sublimes readily

at room temperature when the pressure is reduced. It reacts with hydrogen at 400° C.

$$XeF_4 + 2H_2 \rightarrow Xe + 4HF$$

It reacts with mercury

$$XeF_4 + 4Hg \rightarrow Xe + 2Hg_2F_2$$

and undergoes hydrolysis in water or sodium hydroxide solution to yield a complex mixture of products.

X-ray diffraction studies on xenon tetrafluoride have shown that the compound has a square planar configuration. This structure can be simply rationalized in terms of the following octahedral electronic formula

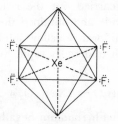

in which two opposite vertices of the octahedron are occupied by unshared electron pairs on the xenon atom.

In addition to the tetrafluoride, xenon also forms a more volatile difluoride, XeF_2, which has a linear configuration which may be assigned the electronic formula.

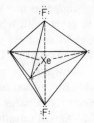

When a large stoichiometric excess of fluorine is heated in a nickel vessel with xenon at 300° C. under 60 atmospheres pressure for an extended period of time, a colorless, crystalline compound having the molecular formula XeF_6 is obtained. This substance melts to a yellow liquid at 46° C. and reacts vigorously with hydrogen at 25° C.

$$XeF_6 + 3H_2 \rightarrow Xe + 6HF$$

It is believed to have an octahedral structure.

Xenon trioxide, a colorless, volatile crystalline compound with the molecular formula XeO_3 is obtained by the hydrolysis of the hexafluoride and the tetrafluoride. The trioxide is violently explosive.

In addition to these compounds there is recent evidence for xenon dichloride, $XeCl_2$. Krypton tetrafluoride, KrF_4, and krypton difluoride, KrF_2, have been prepared, and there is experimental evidence for the formation of an only slightly volatile fluoride of radon.

Thus, it is clear that the elements of the helium family may no longer properly be called the "inert gases." The currently rapid development of this area of research promises further rapid expansion in the chemistry of this family. It is interesting to note, furthermore, that the results of calculations based on the ionization energies of the elements of the helium family and electronegativities of the halogen compounds as well as other atomic parameters correlate well with the experimental findings given above, so that recent discoveries in this area do not argue against presently held theoretical principles, but rather show that these principles had not prior to 1962 been rigorously applied to the elements of the helium family.

CONCLUDING STATEMENT

It is unfortunate (at least, the author has allowed himself so to think) that just now, when we have come to the point where we can begin to rationally predict the properties of substances from the structures of their atoms and from the positions of their atoms in the Periodic Chart, space limitations force us to conclude this book. The author must, therefore, be satisfied simply to point out in summary that answers to three questions have been attempted:

(1) What is the relationship of the Periodic Law to the electronic structures of the atoms?

(2) What atomic parameters determine the kinds of bonds which atoms form with each other, and how do these parameters vary with electronic structure and position of the element in the Periodic Chart?

(3) How are the properties of substances related to the kinds of bonds which unite the atoms of which the substances are composed?

Having reasonably valid answers to these questions the chemist is able to make intelligent estimates of the properties of substances which he has not observed, and furthermore, can design new substances which will approximate a specific set of predetermined properties.

It is the hope of the author that the student will begin to practice the principles herein described and will thus take a first step toward becoming a "chemical architect" in his own right.

INDEX